Cotton Mills of Preston

The Power Behind the Thread

T . C . DICKINSON

Carnegie Publishing Ltd, 2002

First published in 2002 by
Carnegie Publishing Ltd
Carnegie House, Chatsworth Road
Lancaster LA1 4SL
Publishing website: www.carnegiepub.co.uk
Book production website: www.wooof.net

Copyright © T.C. Dickinson, 2002

British Library Cataloguing-in-Publication data
A CIP record for this book is available from the British Library

ISBN 1-85936-096-3

Typeset by Carnegie Publishing
Printed and bound in the UK by
the Alden Press, Oxford

Contents

Abbreviations

ihp   indicated horsepower, which is the horsepower generated
inside an engine's cylinder

rpm revolutions per minute

psi   pounds per square inch (pressure)

List of Illustrations

List of Illustrations

Maps (1912) of Preston showing sites of cotton mills

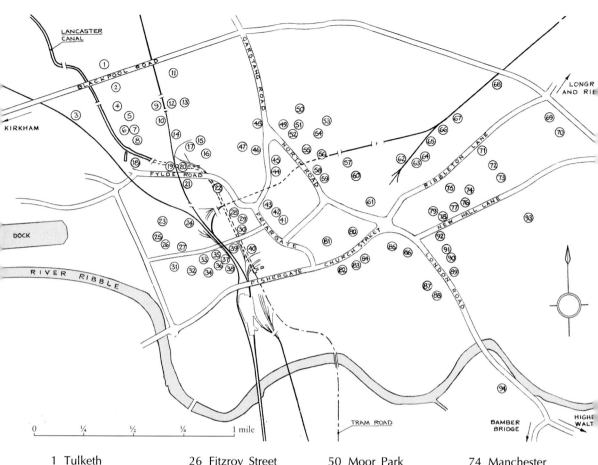

1	Tulketh	26	Fitzroy Street	50	Moor Park	74	Manchester
2	Embroidery	27	Hunt Street	51	Southgate	75	Hartford
3	Ashton Shed	28	Canal Street	52	Broomfield	76	India
4	Stocks Bridge	29	Edward Street	53	Brunswick Place	77	Alliance Works
5	Parker Street	30	Bridge Street	54	Kent Street	78	Centenary
6	Shelley Road	31	Victoria (near The	55	Hanover Street	79	New Preston
7	Brookhouse		New Quay)	56	Bute	80	Pole Street
8	Progress	32	Bow Lane	57	Astley Field	81	Lord Street
9	Bold Street	33	Markland Street	58	Park Lane	82	Avenham Street
10	Raglan	34	Arthur Street	59	Sedgewick St Shed	83	Willow Street
11	Moor Hall	35	Kay Street	60	St Paul's Road	84	Grimshaw Street
12	Queen's	36	Caledonian	61	Hopwood Street	85	Yard Works
13	Oxheys	37	Pitt Street	62	Victoria (Peel Hall St)	86	Sovereign
14	Aqueduct	38	Ribble Street	63	Peel	87	Stourton
15	Springfield	39	Cable Street	64	Wellington	88	Frenchwood
16	Arkwright	40	Heatley Street	65	Deepdale	89	Bank Top
17	Murray Street	41	Back Lane	66	Lutwidge	90	Fishwick
18	Tulketh Factory	42	Walker Street	67	Alexandra	91	Primrose
19	Steam	43	Moor Lane	68	Emerson Road	92	New Hall Lane
20	Fylde Road Shed	44	Bushell Street	69	Tennyson Road	93	Cliff
21	Fylde Road	45	Lawson	70	Waverley Park	94	Flats
22	Moss Shed	46	Castle Street	71	Ribbleton		
23	Wellfield	47	Greenbank	72	Albert		
24	Croft Street	48	Moor Brook	73	New Hall Lane		
25	Spa	49	Brookfield		(Rigby St)		

Introduction

THE LANCASHIRE COTTON INDUSTRY first entered the factory base arena in the 1780s with the introduction of rural water-driven spinning mills. Two decades later, steam power would give rise to the cotton towns, influencing factory design and development, and transforming genteel market places into major industrial centres. Therefore no publication on urban cotton mills can be considered to be complete without mention of this power technology to which the bulk of this book, allied to the Preston industry, bears reference.

As a prime mover the steam engine had a long association with Preston textiles, beginning in the 1790s and ending with the closure of Tulketh Mill in 1968.

Chapter by chapter, decade by decade, this book outlines the role performed by steam power for over a century and a half in Preston's mills. In chronological order it lists every cotton factory to appear on the Preston scene, giving building dates, site layouts, constructional details, spindleage and loomage (where appropriate), ownership, and final closure dates.

It is said that childhood experiences can make a lasting impression, and this was true of my first, and sadly my only, visit to see a Preston mill engine. I remember quite clearly that Sunday morning just after the Second World War being invited by a neighbour who was a 'tackler' at the Brookhouse Mills of J. & A. Leigh in Old Lancaster Lane, to see a mill engine.

Entering the mill yard we passed a boiler house to the right of us with boilers on the simmer in readiness for a Monday morning start, then on into a weaving shed where a sea of cloth upon loom stretched far into the distance. Eventually we arrived in the engine room of the firm's adjacent Progress Mill of 1906 in Shelley Road, and there in all its trappings of Edwardian elegance was the engine, spotless and motionless; a sight indeed to remember.

Mill engine designers were not only first-class engineers, but artists in their own right, and this rare combination of engineering skill and artistic talent was evident in the Progress Mill engine. Researches years later were to focus on the engine having been

1. Map of Preston showing location of the mills

an Ashton, Frost Co. Ltd example from the Bank Top foundry in Blackburn.

At the beginning of the 1970s I visited the cotton mill of Paul Catterall & Sons Ltd in Maitland Street to take photographs for the production of a school-based course in industrial archaeology. The mill had recently closed and a chance invitation to look around the two derelict engine rooms brought to mind that memorable Sunday morning visit to Progress Mill.

Shortly after the Maitland Street factory visit, I became aware that no definitive work had been presented on the history and development of Preston's textile mill steam technology. In 1952 Keith Scott, a Preston architect, had written a Masters thesis entitled *Preston Textile Mills*, which was a superb architectural account but not an in-depth study of the industry's power technology. Indeed throughout the fifties and sixties when the few remaining engines were at work, no attempt was made by any appropriate body to investigate and record this particular aspect of Preston's industrial history. Just before the end of the sixties the town's last surviving engine was scrapped at the Tulketh Spinning Mill in Balcarres Road, leaving behind a very small selection of disused engine houses, boiler houses, condenser ponds and chimneys; all redundant representatives of the steam-driven mill era.

Therefore it was with some urgency that I began primary research in 1971, visiting all the remaining mills, and by the end of the decade I was in a position to submit my Masters thesis 'Preston Mill Engines' to the Department of History of Science and Technology at the University of Manchester Institute of Science and Technology.

In 1983, abridged sections of the thesis appeared in a modest publication by Lancashire Libraries Publishing Service, entitled *Lancashire Under Steam*. Economics were to dictate that only the final chapter would be devoted to the Preston industry. Thus the bulk of my 1979 thesis on Preston engines would remain unpublished and the emergence of more material on the subject during the eighties led me to decide in 1990 that this book was needed.

In retrospect, if research had begun at the start of the nineties this record as it stands today would not have been possible. Mill demolition, the tidying-up bonfire, and the call of the grave, would have denied me the opportunity I had in the seventies. Meeting engine men and mill managers alike, I was able to piece together what must remain a fragmented account of a lost heritage.

T. C. Dickinson

CHAPTER ONE

The First Engines

T HE FIRST APPLICATION of steam power for spinning cotton in Preston was in 1796 at Lord Derby's Dale Street Mill, off Stanley Street. Having commenced work in February, the engine was amongst a number listed later in that year when the Birmingham engine building firm of Boulton & Watt brought about legal action against the makers of the Dale Street Mill engine, Bateman & Sherratt of Manchester, for their pirating of Watt's engine design patents. September 1795 had seen a similar Manchester-built engine started at the calico printing works of Watson, Fielding, Meyers & Company, Preston. This engine and the Dale Street one were of the 'atmospheric' type but had the design improvements of Watt, hence the pirating allegations.

The 'atmospheric' engine had made its debut in 1712 when Thomas Newcomen erected one in a colliery near Dudley Castle in Staffordshire. For the rest of the century it served its purpose well as a pumping engine, but by the 1790s, having been adopted in the textile industry to provide rotary drive, it was fast becoming obsolete.

It was a somewhat crude affair in whichever domain it was set to work, and breakdowns would occur with tiresome regularity. Its open-top, vertically placed cylinder was supplied with steam underneath its piston, the latter having reached the top of its stroke by the weight of the pump rod in the case of a pumping engine. A jet of cold water then effected condensation of the steam so relieving the underside of the piston from as much air pressure as possible, enabling atmospheric pressure from above to push the piston downwards to make the working stroke. To achieve rotary motion, a 'rack and pinion' arrangement, as shown in Figure 3, was used in the textile industry, but by this time the engine had undergone several modifications to make it a viable prime mover.

Such modifications had been introduced from 1768 onwards by James Watt, and by the 1790s he was able to introduce an engine in which the power of steam was the driving force on the piston, with double-acting rotative drive versions available as shown in Figure 4. Other engine builders, unable to copy the heavily patented new engines of Watt, began to adapt the old Newcomen engine for cotton spinning by producing two cylinder versions; one such firm being Bateman & Sherratt of Salford who were Boulton & Watt's main Lancashire competitors. However, the Salford partnership would take to piracy when they decided to fit Watt-type separate condensers and air pumps to their new engines, thus infringing the design patents of Watt.

The engine building partnership of Boulton & Watt which had been formed during the 1770s did not react immediately to the piracy. In fact, it was not until their Lancashire customers pointed out that whilst they had to pay the Birmingham firm's engine premiums, others who had other makes of engines infringing Watt's patents were paying nothing, that Boulton & Watt took positive action. A complete system of espionage was organised in which a team of spies in Lancashire collected affidavits and inspected all the private engines sold by Bateman & Sherratt. Arising from these investigations, information regarding a number of Preston's early engines came to light.

1. Thomas Watson, of Watson, Fielding, Meyers & Co., Calico printers, Preston. Two cylinders, 18in. diam., 3½ft stroke; commenced working September 1795. Bateman & Sherratt were also in the process of erecting another pirate engine for this firm, in place of a 'common engine' previously erected by them.

2. Lord Derby, at Preston; purpose not stated. Two cylinders, 19in. diam., 3½ft. stroke, said to be of 17hp; commenced working February, 1796.

The latter engine had been set up in premises in Dale Street which had been acquired by the Earl of Derby in June 1795, to be known as the Lord's Factory for the spinning and manufacture of cotton. An inventory of November 1796 lists the engine. By this time John Watson had become a tenant in the factory, and in June 1803 purchased the entire premises outright, but the taking on of further loans made him bankrupt in 1807.

Isaac Perrins and John Varley, who among others working on behalf of Boulton & Watt in finding information, had the following to say:

In addition to all the evidence about piracies, we have come across information in this correspondence of a few ordinary atmospheric engines made by Bateman & Sherratt during these years. There was one built for a Mr Norton, dyer, of Salford, and three for Messrs J. & S. Horrocks, Cotton-spinners, Preston, one of which had been working 'some years' while the other two were still erecting (one pirating Watt's parallel motion).

2. The famous 'Yellow Factory', in Dale Street, erected for John Horrocks in 1791, where a horse powered the machinery. (*Harris Museum, Preston*)

Injunctions were eventually obtained against Bateman & Sherratt and others including Watson of Preston on 2 May 1796. Bateman & Sherratt were to pay the premiums of their own engines with interest; deposit their bond for £4,000 as a security against further infringements; furnish an accurate list of the engines constructed upon Watt's patent principles, with the names of the purchasers, the dimensions of the engines etc; pay Boulton & Watt's costs and expenses; and Boulton & Watt were to have liberty to inspect their engines at all times.

After 1796 Bateman & Sherratt still had a good business in atmospheric engines and in 1799 they were copying Boulton & Watt engines exactly, leaving everything ready to put on the condenser as soon as Watt's patent expired just after 1800. In December 1799, as a special concession to Isaac Horrocks, Preston mill owner and cousin of John and Samuel Horrocks, Bateman & Sherratt were allowed to erect an engine with a condenser and air pump for Messrs Newsham & Horrocks of Preston but no general licence was granted, that is presumably until the patents monopoly of Watt ended a short time later.

During his time in Preston as a cotton entrepreneur, John Watson had developed two spinning mills on the town's outskirts at Roach Bridge and Penwortham, and had gone into partnership with William Collinson who had built the first spinning mill in Preston in 1777 in Moor Lane, where the offices of British Telecom now stand. Initially powered by a windmill, then horse power, the mill was eventually to be known as the 'Huzzing Factory' because of the sound of its steam engine, a Boulton & Watt atmospheric type delivered to Watson some time between 1794 and 1797. Shakeshaft's Map of 1809 shows the factory site supporting two large condenser ponds which enabled the cooling of engine condensate by natural evaporation; an essential part of a steam engine's operational cycle and explained in detail in chapter three.

In 1860 the Moor Lane factory was demolished to make way

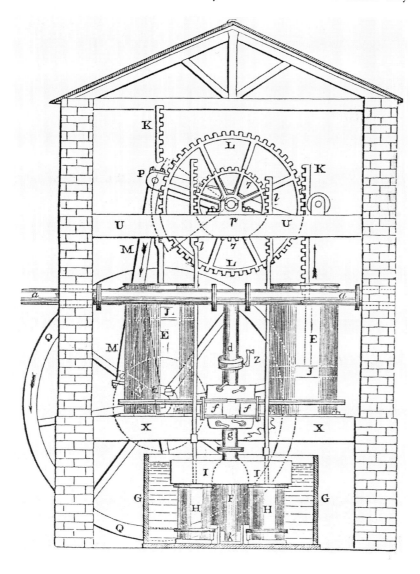

3. A double-acting atmospheric engine for mill work, 1794.

The First Engines

4. A 10 horsepower Boulton & Watt engine with boiler.

for a new works of the gas company, but just prior to demolition its engine, boiler, shafting, doors, windows, and slates were to be auctioned, the engine going for £50.

A report of 11 January of that year in the *Preston Guardian* gave a description of the engine which read:

> The sway-beam is a bulk of red pine, one half of which being cracked is now strongly clamped with iron and screwed together; it had what is called 'hand-gearing' affixed to the cylinder, and the governor balls worked on a rod fixed perpendicularly upon a bracket which is projected from the wall.

Hand-gearing refers to valve handles for hand operation when first starting the engine, to open and close the engine's inlet and outlet steam valves in a precise sequence until sufficient engine stroke and vacuum had been built up, by which time (after several minutes) the engine was capable of working its valves.

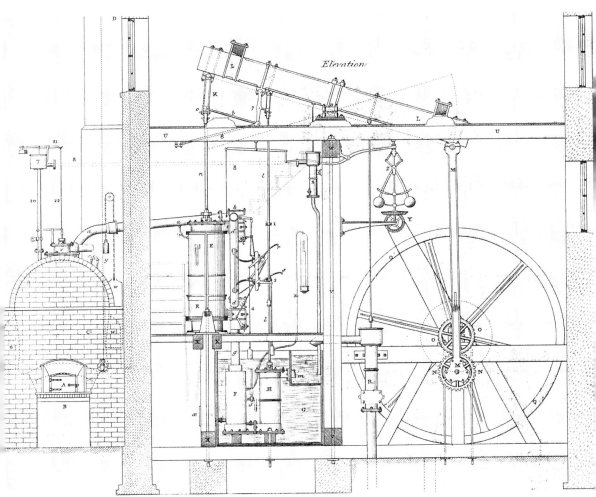

Elevation

John Horrocks came to Preston from Edgeworth near Bolton and was soon to recognise the capabilities of steam power. His first mill in Preston, the 'Yellow Factory', was built near Watson's Lord's Mill by 1792 and was initially horse powered. In 1801, James Watt junior visited Preston to see 'the six or seven engines' operated by Horrocks.

The first Preston cotton factories like their counterparts elsewhere in Lancashire were spinning mills, the mechanisation of the weaving process by steam power not becoming a viable proposition until the mid 1820s. In the meantime, Preston's population of hand-loom weavers, living and working amongst the growing factory communities, enjoyed a reasonable degree of prosperity as steam power was concentrated upon the spinning processes of cotton.

Before 1790, two types of spinning machine had been available. One was Richard Arkwright's water-frame, patented in 1769, and really only suitable as its name implied for water-powered factories because of its heavy construction. The second machine was James Hargreaves's spinning jenny, patented in 1770, but it was more suited to domestic use than a factory machine. During the 1770s, Samuel Crompton developed the spinning mule which would combine the best qualities of the water-frame and the jenny, presenting a machine which could produce a fine and strong thread. However, the mule would not be adopted for factory use until after 1790, and even then a part of its operating procedure would be performed by hand, hence the term 'hand mules'.

In 1797, Ainsworth of Preston, who was a partner in the Watson empire before its crash, placed an order for mules of 372 spindles each from McConnell & Kennedy in Manchester, which with three lines of rollers cost 4s. 6d. per spindle, whilst gearing for water or steam power was 3d. per spindle extra.

Earlier in 1791, Watt had written to Peter Ewart, an engine erector in the Manchester area regarding the power required to drive spinning machinery. Part of the letter read: 'For machine twist we reckon 8 horses power can drive about 700 spindles and preparers, but for fine twist they can do more than double that number'. Six years later a rating of 700 spindles per horsepower seems to have been an accepted figure.

At the end of Preston Guild Year, 1802, about eight spinning factories had been built in the town. Hewitson in his *History of Preston*, published in 1883, writing about the 1802 Guild, states: 'Another interesting display during this Guild consisted of an exhibition of machinery in motion – a steam engine, the first probably worked in Preston, and certain mechanical ...'.

Between 1802 and 1821, only eight mills would be added to the

Preston list partly due to the economic stresses brought about by the French Wars (1793–1815). However, in this long period of war, some expansion would come about in the Preston industry.

John Horrocks, who had been amongst the first group of cotton factory entrepreneurs in Preston, died in 1804 at the early age of thirty six, leaving his brother Samuel to take on the Preston firm on behalf of the trustees; the business continuing to expand in spite of the war years. In 1812, Samuel Horrocks had 107,000 mule spindles in eight mills, and by 1815 the firm was known as Horrockses, Miller & Company; Thomas Miller who was originally from Bolton having been a partner since 1801.

One particular development in support of the Preston industry during the French Wars period, was the setting up of small workshops in some mill yards to supply the factories with machinery for the steam power age. In 1798, for example, Richard Riley and John Paley, who had worked for John Horrocks, went into partnership in the machine making business at Horrocks' Spitals Moss factory site before building their own cotton mill in 1802 in nearby Heatley Street. Paley was to be involved in an iron foundry on the Heatley Street site, whilst Riley went on to develop Bank Top Mill, opposite the Horrocks' Frenchwood factory at the top of London Road.

As the war came to an end, the Preston cotton industry began to prepare for a major phase of expansion.

CHAPTER TWO

Post-War Developments of the 1820s

WRITING in 1821 in his *History of Preston*, Marmaduke Tulket would mention the sixteen Preston factories then in full employment, and list the power ratings of their engines:

Horrocks' Yard (4 factories, 2 engines)	18hp & 24hp
Spital's Moss Mills (Horrocks & Co.)	40hp
Frenchwood Mills (Horrocks & Co., possibly 2 mills)	18hp
Vose & Bleasdale's Mills, Stanley Street	20hp
Church St Mills (Ainsworth, Catterall & Co.)	15hp
Clayton's Mills, Moor Lane	10hp
Kaye's Mills, near Knox Folly (off what was to become Marsh Lane)	18hp
Park & Sons' Mill (Arthur St and Cable St area of Bridge Lane)	18hp
Willow St Mills (J. Swainson) off Church St (this engine was being erected)	36hp
Paley & Co. Mills, Heatley Street	20hp
Canal Bank Mill (John Paley & Co.)	12hp
Back Lane Factory (Caton & Leche)	7hp

Steam boilers would be in the form of the waggon and Cornish type and there was always the risk of a fatal explosion. As the demand for higher working steam pressures rose, so did the death toll of boiler personnel in the Lancashire industry.

Coal supplies for Preston came from the Wigan area via the Lancaster Canal, opened by the early 1800s. Before then, J. Aiken had written in 1795: 'Preston is supplied with coals by means of the Douglas Navigation which enters the Ribble somewhat lower than Walton Bridge, and it will have another source of supply from the new Lancaster Canal'.

Inflation costs brought about by the French Wars were to be responsible for a change in construction of the canal at Preston whereby the waterway would be left in two separate sections, a northern one from Preston to Tewitfield (extended later to

Post-War Developments of the 1820s

Kendal), and a southern section beginning at Aspull near Wigan and terminating at Walton Summit near Bamber Bridge. By 1803, the two ends between Preston and Walton Summit had been connected by a tramway which included three inclined planes. On the tramway, horse-drawn wagons conveyed Wigan district coal to the Preston terminus of the canal, opposite which the Corn Exchange of the 1820s would be built. Further development of this coal distribution network would take place after the arrival of the North Union Railway in 1838.

During the post-war years of the 1820s, new textile mill construction in Preston produced buildings of narrow construction, incorporating cast-iron columns supporting wooden beams onto which were fixed wood flooring. Engine houses in most cases were internal and unattractive architecturally, but there were exceptions. Tulket, describing John Horrocks' Canal Street Mill of 1799, and which was sixteen windows long and stood six storeys high, stated: 'Adjoining this extensive factory on the site next to the canal, a fine steam engine house presents itself, built of free stone, with a towering brick chimney'.

Underlying clays encouraged local brick manufacture to supply programmes of mill construction and associated housing in Preston for most of the nineteenth century, with stone sills, lintels etc. being supplied by quarries in nearby Longridge.

A typical new cotton factory of 1820s Preston was Brunswick Place Mill, off Kent Street, operational by 1825. Its four-storey

5. Brunswick Mill, sometimes referred to as Brunswick Place Mill, was operational by 1825, and would be a typical Preston cotton mill of the period, with limited and small windows due to the need for the walls to be load-bearing and therefore quite substantial.
(*Harris Museum, Preston*)

block housed spinning, carding, warping and winding machinery. At one end was a spiral staircase tower, whilst on the northern wall and rising through the roof was the mill's short, square sectioned chimney. Internally, a central row of cast-iron columns acted as wedges between the principal wooden beams which spanned the full width of the block, side walls being load-bearing thus offering limited window area.

Edward Street Mill, long since gone and which stood near the present university, was built in the same decade as Brunswick Place Mill and had similar constructional characteristics. The engine house was at the north end of Edward Street Mill on the first floor, situated directly above the boiler house. In contrast was the huge cotton factory of Swainson & Birley at Fishwick, erected in about 1823 and known as the 'Big Factory'.

Gas supplies for lighting the mills had become fairly well established in this decade. In 1827 four or five cotton manufacturers formed the Union Gas Company in opposition to the town's original Company of 1815. The partial adoption of meters came about for the first time, and in 1834 an effort was made to bring meters into greater use, except for mill proprietors and occupiers of front shops; the factories were looked upon as an exception because of the regulated time of working by Act of Parliament. The Union Gas Company remained until 1839 when negotiations for its sale were opened, resulting in a transfer to the Preston Gas Company which had installed its first gas holder in Walker Street in 1834. By the late 1880s, three gas manufacturing stations were in existence, Glover Street, Walker Street, and Moor Lane, containing 574 retorts and 9 gas holders. Two gas holder stations were also established; one in Ribbleton Lane, the other at Walton, whilst two of Preston's largest cotton mill complexes, Yard Works and New Preston Mills, each had a gasometer on site.

The first power looms in Preston appeared in 1824 at Paley's Heatley Street Mill; a technological breakthrough for the town's manufacturers but not appreciated by the hand loom weavers.

In 1785, the Rev. Dr Edmund Cartwright had invented a power loom but this was to prove unsuccessful. Throughout the 1790s attempts to introduce power looms were dogged by mechanical problems, the obstacle to success being the necessity to stop frequently to dress the warp as it unrolled from the beam; an operation which required manpower and thereby no saving of expense. Messrs Radcliffe & Ross of Stockport were eventually to produce a dressing machine to overcome the problem, patents being taken out in 1803 and 1804, after which the power loom became a viable proposition.

Another breakthrough for the cotton industry was the introduction of self-acting mules from 1830 onwards. In the self-actor, the mechanism was such that the spindle carriage rolled in and out at the proper speed without the need for manual operation. Although a self-actor had been made by Kelly in 1792, the machine did not meet with success until Richard Roberts of Manchester produced one whose mechanism offered precisely what was needed. For this machine, Roberts was to take out a patent in 1825 with a second one in 1830 following further developmental work on it.

However, the Preston industry would be cautious in adopting the self-acting mule, with only Rodgett's Bow Lane Mill and Dawson's Oxheys Mill in Aqueduct Street having them in 1842. In fact, many of the town's mills would operate hand mules for years afterwards, the last ones to be scrapped being those at Hincksman's Croft Street Mill in the late 1880s.

Several Preston firms such as Ainscow & Tomlinson, Munday's, Sleddon's, and Grundy's made mules; the latter making a good light hand mule capable of producing nearly 23,000 draws per week of 36s weft at ten hours a day. For well into the second half of the century, the hand mule had the reputation for producing fine yarns which is most probably the reason why the Preston masters held onto their hand mules for so long. Neste, as late as 1865 was to write:

> Self-acting mules are applicable from the coarsest numbers up to 110, but they are seldom found in use for finer numbers than 80. The finer yarns are spun on hand mules.

But as self-acting mules increased in numbers, the local machine shops did not follow up with improvements to their mule designs and their reputation decreased, with firms such as Dobson & Barlow of Bolton and Platt Bros of Oldham taking advantage of a growing market demand for the new type mules; Dobson & Barlow were making self-actors by 1850. In 1880, Eli Spencer of Platt Bros was able to write:

> For spinning yarns of medium fine counts, say up to 90, the self-acting mule has now almost entirely superseded the hand mule. The work is excellent, both in quality and quantity.

During the 1830s, experiments relating to the new self-acting mules and power looms, and the need to drive them by steam engines, had been carried out in certain Manchester mills. One set of results showed that to drive 396 power looms and 16 dressing machines, 66 horsepower was required; whilst 1,080 spindles in 3 self-acting mules needed 2.59 horsepower.

CHAPTER THREE

Enterprise and Expansion (1830–1850)

MYERS' 1836 town map of Preston shows in the region of thirty-five cotton mills and a small number of flax mills. Quite a number of foundries had been established by this time, one being the Soho Foundry of Joseph Clayton in Greenbank Street, established in the previous year to specialise in boilers, gas apparatus and engines. John Stevenson & Company of Canal Bank Foundry in Fylde Road was another firm of boiler makers which by 1837 was connected with steam engine building. With this technology available the stage was set for the second phase of expansion of the developing cotton industry in Preston.

On 27 February 1836 an article on the development and improvement of Preston was printed in the *Preston Chronicle*, part of which read:

> To commence with the enlargement of the town; – on the north side nearly the whole of what is known as the Green Bank Estate (the property of Messrs T. & W. Tomlinson), extending from Moor Lane and Fylde Street northward to the Moor Park brook, comprising an area of about 34 acres, is laid out in streets, some of which, on the south side, are already filled up with handsome small houses. The whole of this land, which has long been occupied as gardens and small fields and forms an airy and salubrious eminence rising towards the middle will, probably in a year or two, become a sort of new town, or compact manufacturing district, and the neatness and convenience of the houses will, we doubt not, render it the favourite residence of a large portion of our operative community, for whom it is principally intended. The works in which this population will find employment, will, for the most part, be situated along the valley of the brook before alluded to, on the north side, and beyond which is the open country. The supply of water afforded by the brook, as well as by springs and streamlets on each side, together with other local advantages, render this valley a peculiarly suitable site for a considerable number of cotton works ... One mill on the estate (Mr Crankshaw's) is already completed, at the north east corner, and near the junction of Moor Lane with the Lancaster Road. Continuous on the east side of that road is the new mill built by Messrs Sleddon &

Enterprise and Expansion (1830—1850)

Threlfall. A little to the west of Mr Crankshaw's, and on the top of the brow, another extensive mill is being erected by Mr Hawkins – the bricks made and burnt on its very site, and the lodge almost ready formed by a natural hollow in the hill. Three other mills, it is anticipated, will, ere long, be built near the brook further west, and beyond these on the other side of the canal (under which the road passes by a tunnel or aqueduct) stand the three recently built mills, the property respectively of Mr Dawson, Mr Dewhurst and Mr W. Taylor.

This account tells of the formation of the Adelphi area, street after street of terraced housing, of which Bedford Street and Byrom Street were amongst a number which traversed the main thoroughfare of Adelphi Street, which descended to Aqueduct Street on the valley floor of the Moor Brook after passing alongside the reservoir wall of Hawkins's Greenbank Mills.

Crankshaw's Mill mentioned in the article was Moor Brook Mill sited opposite the Unicorn Inn, and Sleddon's and Threlfall's factory was Broomfield Mill, erected in 1835. The three mills to 'be built near the brook further west', would eventually be William Dawson's Oxheys Mill in Aqueduct Street erected at the beginning of the 1840s; Thomas McGuffog's Murray Street Mill built about the same time; and John and Adam Leigh's Brookhouse Mill of 1844.

6. Overleaf:
Preston in the mid-1840s, from the Ordnance Survey first edition map of that period.

Below:
A detail from the same map showing substantial cotton mill development in rural north and north-west Preston during the 1840s.

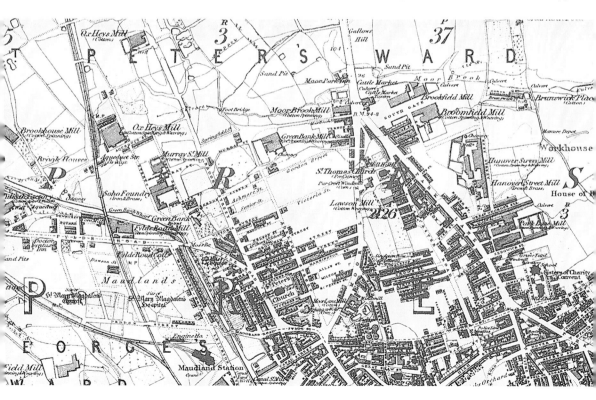

15

Of 'the three recently built mills' mentioned, the first was Hugh and Arthur Dawson's mill in Fylde Road and backing onto the canal. The second, the property of Mr Dewhurst, was a builder's supply works, whilst the third mill was Tulketh Factory, built in 1835.

By 1836, Preston's population had risen to 36,000 but the greatest expansion was yet to come. To the east lay the rural environs of the New Preston area; to the north west was the open expanse of the Mandland Estate; whilst northwards just beyond the Moor Brook, lay the moor itself. All three areas were soon to be transformed into grid like patterns of housing within whose monotonous sprawl would be the new mills of the forties and fifties and beyond.

During the 1820s and 1830s, the Preston and District hand loom industry had been extensive, and at one particular period about 4,000 operatives had been in its employment. Local maps show row upon row of these weaving communities in Preston with their cellar workrooms, and although the trade had entered its decline by the beginning of the 1840s, hand loom manufacture was still surviving in the town, especially within its central area. The 1841 Trade Directory lists a number of loom workshops tucked away just off the main thoroughfares, for example in Mount Street, Chapel Walk, and Gorst's Court.

With the arrival of steam-driven power looms in Preston during the 1820s, its textile industry was given the impetus it needed for further expansion. In the 1841 Trade Directory, twenty-three establishments are recorded for the cotton and muslin manufacturers, while for the cotton spinners only, and combined cotton spinners and power loom manufacturers, twenty-five firms are represented.

The 'Power Loom Stock of Machinery' for 30 June 1839, at Horrocks' Yard Works lists for Weaving Room number one:

48¾ looms with 2 shuttles each, temples, rods, straps,
weights, ropes, shuttle boxes, weight and waste
boxes, complete –   £312 0s. 0d.

98⅞ looms with 2 shuttles each, with as above,
complete –   £576 0s. 0d.

1 gas lighting lamp –   £0 1s. 0d.

On the same site in 1836 an engine house had been erected for the new Field Mill, and for 30 June 1840, the Loom Stock Book List for its weaving room mentions:

120 new shuttles   £10 0s. 0d.

12 gallons of sperm oil   £4 16s. 0d.

30lbs of tallow   15s. 0d.

7. The Adelphi Street and Aqueduct Street area, showing Greenbank Mill, a rebuild of the early 1860s, almost surrounded by mill workers' housing. Adelphi Street runs diagonally in the lower half of the photographs. This is an archetypcal urban landscape of the 'heroic' age of the industrial revolution as seen and condemned by commentators of the age from Dickens to Engels.

With reference to the sperm oil, before mineral oils were introduced sperm whale oil was used in considerable amounts in textiles for lubricating the machinery.

The use of power looms brought about a demand for a stronger warp thread which the 'throstle', a new spinning machine based on Arkwright's water frame, could provide and which was stronger in fact than the mule could produce. Quite a number of throstles were installed in Preston but the mule was in more general use in the town's mills, such as it was throughout the Lancashire industry, because its cop held about three times as much yarn as was on the bobbin of a throstle. This meant less work for the winder and also less labour for the doffer.

On the motive power side during this period, it was usual to fit a single cylinder beam engine for small powers, and a double version, that is a pair of single cylinder engines working on the same crankshaft, for large powers; a practice which continued throughout the fifties and sixties in Preston.

In 1841, near the town centre, Lord Street Mill was erected and fitted with an engine, presumably the one still working in the 1890s when it was listed along with other Preston engines in a 'Classification of Mills for Assessment Purposes' compiled by

8. A pair of beam engines at Yard Works, drawn by Worthington & Company, Preston, 1 January 1855. (*Harris Museum, Preston*)

9. A pair of 'McNaughted' beam engines with geared drive: a typical layout of motive power in a number of Preston mills at one period.

Enterprise and Expansion (1830—1850)

Myres, Veevers & Myres, Valuers. Under the title of 'Preston Union Mill Valuations and Plans, 1896–97' reference D74 PRE, this classification, now in the Harris Reference Library, Preston, is the only detailed list of Preston's mill engines of the nineteenth century found to date. Complete with scaled layouts of the textile mills then in operation, it has been invaluable in tracing engine development in Preston within this period.

The Lord Street engine listed in 1897 was a single cylinder beam engine developing 76 indicated horsepower at 32rpm with a 25″ diameter cylinder bore and a 6′ stroke. Spindles in operation for making weft amounted to 11,280, and although the mill's machinery required 22 horsepower, and the power available from the engine after transmission was 24 horsepower, the power being used actually 25; a possible indication that the engine was verging on overload. A second-hand boiler from Bolton, apparently bringing about a saving of £250, was steaming at 25 psi pressure, and consuming 80 tons of coal per month.

10. A plan of Brookhouse Mill in the 1890s.

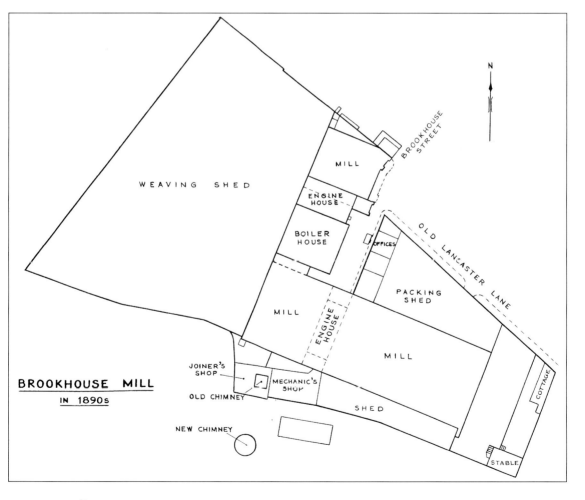

BROOKHOUSE MILL
IN 1890s

Enterprise and Expansion (1830—1850)

11. Brookhouse Mill of 1844, with the typical style of water tower for the period. On the right is the multi-storey block of 1858.

12. The multi-storey block of 1858 at Brookhouse Mill, with the beam engine house on the left. The engine was later to be pusher-compounded.

Contrasting in size to the Lord Street Mill engine in 1897, was the double beam engine layout at the Brookhouse Mills of 1844, on the north-western side of Preston in Old Lancaster Lane. Installed as a pair of single cylinder engines by Rothwell of Bolton, each engine would be 'McNaughted' in 1882 by the Preston engine and boiler making firm of Joseph Clayton.

McNaughting was a term used for compounding a single cylinder beam engine to increase its power whereby a high pressure cylinder exhausting into the original cylinder, now the low pressure cylinder, was fitted between the beam support columns and the crankshaft. Piston loads were thus opposed as when the low pressure piston was pulling the oscillating beam downwards, the new high pressure piston was pushing the beam upwards and vice versa, so reducing stresses about the beam centre. William McNaught of Bury had patented the idea in 1845, and in the same year William Fairburn introduced the twin flue Lancashire boiler which became the standard boiler in the Lancashire textile industry. The improved steam-raising capabilities of the new boiler enabled 'McNaughting' to be carried out on engines throughout the 1870s and 1880s as higher working pressures became available.

The pair of McNaughted engines driving mills 1 and 2 at Brookhouse in 1896 must have been an impressive sight. Positioned

in an internal engine room with a mill block on either side, one of the engines had 30″ and 35½″ diameter cylinder bores on respective strokes of 3′ and 6′. At 28 rpm and working on corresponding average steam pressures of 55 and 14 psi, respective ihps of 124 and 140 were being developed. For the second engine which had the same bores and strokes, respective ihps amounted to 213 and 217.

An 'Assessment of Valuation' for *c*. 1844 mentions a number of Preston factories, giving the name of their owners and engine horsepower which appear in brackets in the following:

Pitt Street (Clayton, 20), Fylde Road (Dawson, 56), Greenbank (Hawkins, 55), Heatley Street (Paley, 79), Stanley Street (Paley, 18), North Road (P. Catterall & Son, 140), Hanover Street (Sleddon, 90), Tulketh Factory (Taylor, 64).

The Greenbank engine was valued at £1,875 and the Pitt Street one of c1826 was worth £500.

On 16 May 1845, Mr L. Horner, Factory Inspector for the district reported: '... there are many new factories now building or nearly completed. At Preston alone there are eight, two of them with 100 horses power each, one with 95, one with 50, three with 30 and one with 20; in all 455 horses.'

Two of the largest mills were to be combined concerns, that is establishments for spinning and weaving, and the remaining six for spinning only. The claims of the inspector were derived from the 'New Investments of Capital in Factories' for the District from 1 January 1844, to 30 April 1845. There was mention of a first supply and an increased supply of gas for the following winter for twenty one mills in Preston, and the gas company was consequently extending its works. Also reported was the establishing of new weaving sheds in Preston for power looms, the inspector recording two such establishments as: 'A new weaving shed and a new engine of 50 horses ... New weaving shed with a new 20 horse engine.'

Initial experiences in the use of power looms had proved that they worked better on ground floors than on upper floors because the damp conditions at ground floor level provided the necessary humidity for the free working of the cotton thread. Also the transportation to and from the looms of the heavy beams onto which the warp thread was wound, would have presented immense practical difficulties if multi-storey weaving factories had become common. Expensive and heavily reinforced floors in such buildings would have been necessary to support the tremendous weight of looms.

Therefore, the introduction of power looms brought about

13. Warping frames and beaming machine at Horrocks' Yard Works. On the left the warp thread is being wound onto the 'reel like' beam before being taken to the looms; the tremendous weight of a full beam was one reason why loomage was arranged only on the ground floors of mills. (*Harris Museum, Preston*)

another architectural feature of the cotton industry, the shed principle, whereby looms were placed in ground floor sheds. Their saw-toothed roofing incorporating north-facing windows and south-facing slate surfaces ensured the interiors remained relatively cool but reasonably well lit in daytime conditions. Not many years ago one could see this building technique having been employed on the valley floor of Preston's Moor Brook by way of the old weaving sheds of Brookfield, Moor Brook, and Aqueduct Street Mills. Gradually the whole manufacturing process of winding, beaming, weaving, and sizing would be developed on horizontal lines, that is, on ground level as in the new manufactories (weaving mills) of the early 1900s.

The year 1845 saw the erection of another engine house at Yard Works. This was a time when steam power was being looked upon by many factory owners as a means of reducing working hours whilst at the same time maintaining profit margins.

Horner, in his report of 1845, tells of one Preston mill owner from Manchester, who had two mills in Preston, one for spinning and the other for weaving on power looms. The mill owner was said to have stated in a letter to the Chairman of a meeting at the Corn Exchange in Preston, that he was satisfied that both as much yarn and power loom cloth could be produced at low cost in eleven as in twelve hours per day from his experience over the past year in his mills in Preston.

The first railway line to reach Preston had been the North Union from Wigan in 1838. In 1840, lines to Longridge, Fleetwood, and Lancaster were opened followed by railway connection to Bolton in 1841, Blackburn in 1846, and Liverpool via Ormskirk in 1849. The latter line greatly improved the raw cotton supply route from this major cotton port to Preston, and with direct rail links to prominent centres of industry and more efficient access to the coalfields of south Lancashire, the Preston industry was in a much-favoured position for growth. Its coal supply depot, established years previously at the canal terminus area, could now be extended directly into the mill districts by the formation of railway sidings at Greenbank and Deepdale.

An article on the new found efficiency of railway transit appeared in the *Preston Chronicle*:

On Thursday afternoon last, Mr W. Taylor, cotton manufacturer of Preston, purchased a considerable quantity of cotton from Messrs Bateson & Sons, Liverpool, which was sent by Messrs Tattersall & Clare, Mr Taylor's brokers, to Mr J. Hargreaves, jun., to be conveyed to Preston by the North Union Railway; and, although it did not actually leave Liverpool till after three o'clock yesterday, (Friday morning) it was delivered at Tulketh Factory at eight minutes past nine o'clock, and before eleven o'clock part of it had passed through the several operations of mixing, scutching, sapping, carding, drawing, slubbing, roving and spinning. At half past eleven o'clock, a portion of it was made into cloth by the power-loom; and at twenty minutes past four o'clock in the afternoon, three and a half yards of good, perfect skirting cloth was forwarded by Mr Taylor to Messrs Tattersall & Clare, by the train leaving Preston at twenty minutes past four, and would, in course, be delivered to them before seven o'clock the same evening ... How forcibly does this fact remind us that we live in the age of enterprise – in the very millennium of railway velocity!

Charles Dickens visited Preston in the 1840s so he could gain impressions of an industrial strike. In his novel *Hard Times* published in 1854, 'Coketown' was apparently Preston and within one of the well known extracts from the novel there is a superb literary description of the beam engine at work: '... It had a black canal in it, and a river that ran purple with ill-smelling dye, and vast piles of buildings full of windows where there was a rattling and a trembling all day long, and where the piston of the steam-engine worked monotonously up and down, like the head of an elephant in a state of melancholy madness.'

The map of Preston and District surveyed between 1844 and

1847 and produced to a scale of six inches to one mile, fully illustrated the amount of factory development that had taken place over the past half century. Wellfield Mill, near the Marsh, and Oxheys Mill alongside which would be Ripon Street, are both shown in relative rural environs, whilst Ribbleton Lane Mill on the eastern side of the town centre is somewhat isolated in an undeveloped area, but not for long. Detailed planning of densely populated working class housing would transform large extracts of green land into a dense industrial sprawl over the next two decades.

By the end of the 1840s, a balloon ascent over Preston would have revealed an almost Venetian air about the scene due to a growing number of cotton mill condenser ponds or lodges as they were often referred to. By the time the town map for 1889 had gone to print their numbers had almost reached the hundred mark.

Unlike in Blackburn and Burnley, for example, where quite a number of mills relied upon canal water for engine condensate cooling and condenser feed, the majority of Preston's factories had their own cooling ponds. Only mills in the Brookhouse and Bridge Lane (Marsh Lane) areas would use the Lancaster Canal for condensing purposes. Thus a dominating feature of Preston would be its factory reservoirs bounded by high stone walls which offered yet another architectural dimension arising from King Cotton's reign in the town.

On leaving the final cylinder (or the two, low pressure ones as in the case of a four cylinder triple expansion type – see chapter eight) of an engine, the spent steam entered the engine's condenser where a jet of cold water from the mill reservoir condensed it back to water. This condensate plus air was then pumped by the engine to the reservoir for further cooling by natural evaporation, thus ensuring a constant cold water feed to the condenser. The removal of condensate and air from the engine established an essential partial vacuum on the exhaust side of the cylinders' pistons. Without this vacuum an engine would cease to run, the pressure difference on opposite faces of the pistons not being great enough. The colder the injection water, the greater the vacuum achieved with its affect on engine performance. Changes in atmospheric pressure would affect the efficiency of the engine's air pump or pumps, thus dictating the amount of condensate and air removed and thus the degree of vacuum attained. So much was the influence of climatic variations on engine vacuum, engine men could forecast a change in the weather simply by observing changes in engine performance which directly affected coal consumption, as could be noted at Tulketh Mill in Balcarres Road where 110 tons per week was used in the winter months compared to 75 tons per week in the summer.

It was usual for a mill to have at least two reservoirs; a hot lodge where the condensate was first circulated, and a cold lodge where final circulation took place and from which condenser feed was drawn. Large reservoirs such as those at Yard Works and New Preston Mills were divided into pens to assist circulation. The site area for these industrial lagoons varied from mill to mill according to size of engine plant and space available. At Bank Top Mill about one third of the site was allotted for the two lodges with a similar proportion at Bold Street Mill for its three lodges, whilst at Kent Street Mill two lodges occupied a quarter of the site area.

One of the largest reservoirs was at Fishwick Mills where water rights were established for street surface water to feed into it, water depth being fourteen feet. In some instances, reservoirs were sited some distance from the mill; Pole Street Mill, for example, had its lodge in nearby Bell Street, whilst Aqueduct Street Mill had one of its lodges a block away between Bold Street and Greenbank Street.

For jet condenser feed, twenty five to thirty times the weight of water was needed for the weight of steam used (depending upon feed water temperature) which for a large engine could be 11 to 12 lbs weight of steam per ihp per hour, and the aim was to have the water capacity of a reservoir facility equal to the volume of water injected into the condenser per day. Even though filters were used, piston lubricating oil contaminated the reservoirs, settling on the bottom as a thick sediment, and about every ten years a reservoir would be drained and the sludge removed.

One Preston mill to be denied a place in the nineties classification was Thomas McGuffog's Murray Street Mill, destroyed by fire in November 1885, with the loss of 43,344 spindles. Fortunately a valuation of the mill, its boilers and engines etc., dated 6 May 1876, is now in the care of the Lancashire Record Office, reference DP445. Although the factory was absent from the 1841 Trade Directory, it was in production by 1842 for J. & W. McGuffog who employed fourteen spinners on hand mules. Thomas & William McGuffog were there in 1851, and in the early 1880s, the workforce was made up of 180 hands.

The valuation of 1876 had been compiled by John Hoyle, licensed valuer of Bolton, who valued the stone engine bed, measuring 34′ × 13′ × 20′, at £442. The description of the engines was a rather fragmented one but supposedly adequate for a valuation.

2 Beam Engines 35 horsepower each, one slide valve, one D valve,

14. Elevations and plan of a set of Lancashire boilers, complete with an economiser.

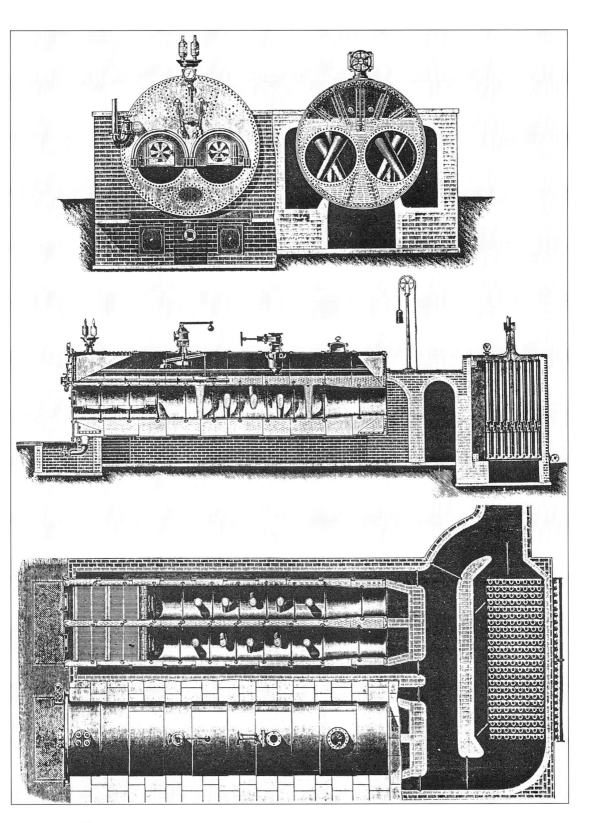

29

HIGH-CLASS LANCASHIRE STEEL BOILERS.
30 FEET LONG, AND UP TO 9 FEET 6 INCHES DIAMETER
WORKING PRESSURES UP TO 220 POUNDS PER SQUARE INCH.

17 (above). An advertisement for Joseph Foster & Sons, Soho Foundry, Preston.
(Harris Museum, Preston)

15 (opposite, top). Workers at Queens Mill posing for a photograph seemingly in front of the boiler house in the mill yard *(Harris Museum, Preston)*

16 (opposite, bottom). Transportation by traction engine of a Lancashire boiler from the works of J. Foster & Sons Ltd.
(Harris Museum, Preston)

cylinders 33″ and 31″ × 6′ stroke, fit up with large segment wheel in middle and large flywheel on 4 columns.

2 Horizontal Steam Engines 20 hp ea, compounded to Beam Engines, cylinders 18½″, 3ft stroke, slide valves.

Here was an engine layout comprising a four-columned beam engine made up of a pair of McNaughted engines, each coupled to a single cylinder horizontal engine termed a pusher.

The practice of fitting a horizontal engine to a single cylinder beam engine was an alternative to McNaughting. But as was the case at Murray Street Mill, where the original beam engines had already been McNaughted, pusher compounding, had raised the motive power yet again without a complete and expensive engine change, which would have entailed an extensive shut down of the factory. A pusher engine was generally fitted to an extension of a beam engine's crankshaft or crankpin, and in some situations the pusher was placed in an adjoining engine room. Because the added impulses of the pusher came between the ones from the original engine, the turning moment of the new combination was an improvement. Quite a number of Preston mills decided to pusher compound their beam engines from the early seventies onwards when horizontal engines became available with higher working steam pressures.

The spinning block at Murray Street Mill had five storeys, the first level accommodating the cardroom, and the fifth one being number four spinning room. The staircase tower was 29 feet round, and the number of petties (toilets) with soil pit, five of which were situated throughout the five storeys, with a large one at the end of the mill, were typical of the time. Boiler house, scutching room, and cotton mixing room, all vulnerable to the fire hazard, were in a three-storey fireproof section, and there was also a two-storey cotton warehouse which had a large arched entrance.

The boiler house had three Lancashire boilers valued at £360 each, 7′ 6″ diameter × 28′ in length, and fitted with Galloway tubes.

In a Lancashire boiler, these tubes (see Figure 14) crossed each furnace tube, thus allowing boiler water passage across the direct heat of the furnace gases and receive additional heat. On leaving the furnace tubes, the furnace gases passed underneath the boiler by a central flue to the front end where they were divided to run back along the sides of the boiler via two side flues which led into the chimney flue. Here was situated the economiser, a nest of cast-iron pipes 4″ diameter × 10′ in height, through which boiler feed water from the engine condenser was pumped to receive heat from the flue gases, thus achieving good steam raising economy. The economiser had been patented in 1845 by Edward Green of Wakefield, and for it to work efficiently, the soot which would accumulate on the pipes had to be removed regularly by mechanical scrapers working off a steam driven mechanism.

At Murray Street Mill, the economiser unit had 120 pipes and with its brickwork was valued at £240, whilst the 40 yard high square, brick chimney complete with stone top, and its flues, were estimated to be worth £245. Overall, the gaslights, steam piping, mill gearing, boilers, engines, and building, mentioned in the valuation, had a total value of almost £41,000.

Two reservoirs were at the bottom of Greenbank Street, alongside Aqueduct Street, the 'hot' lodge measuring 92 feet × 62 feet and 8 feet in depth, whilst the 'cold' lodge measured 122 feet × 64 feet and also 8 feet in depth. The boundary walls of the reservoirs had an inner wall of brick and an outer one (facing the street) of stone. Associated with this 'cooling by evaporation system' of engine condensate were the troughs within which the water was directed during the various stages of the cooling process. At Murray Street Mill there were 225′ of wooden troughing, 2′ × 8″ in section, and 150′ of iron troughing with a sectional measurement of 3′ × 8″.

CHAPTER FOUR

Mid-Century Developments

THE ADVANTAGE of Britain being the first in the field with the mill system had achieved its maximum effect by the early 1830s; during the long peace which followed the Napoleonic Wars we rendered our mechanical knowledge to the rest of the world.

In 1843 the enactment prohibiting the export of British cotton machinery was repealed with the result of more cotton mill building abroad. India was to build her first mills mainly in Bombay during the 1850s, and many a Lancashire-built engine would be destined for foreign parts. Even Lancashire stone for engine beds went out with the engines, often from Whittle quarries near Chorley where the stone was sent to Liverpool for shipment. This guaranteed that the stone was readily available at the time of engine installation; such was the efficiency of Lancashire workmanship and organisation.

As mid-century approached, Britain's cotton industry was still the largest in the world with Lancashire at its heart, but ground was gradually being lost to overseas competition. In Lancashire, specialisation in spinning and weaving was taking place, with spinning predominantly in the Bolton and North Manchester areas, and weaving in East Lancashire; although over fifty per cent of cotton workers were still employed in combined weaving and spinning establishments.

In Preston, the power loom weaving introduced by the cotton spinners, meant that combined concerns were in the majority by mid century.

The mill-building fervour of the 1840s in Preston was to continue throughout the fifties, the New Preston district east of the town seeing much of this industrial development and allocation of associated housing. The first factory in this district was Ribbleton Lane Mill shown for cotton weaving on the town map surveyed between 1844 and 1847; the mill's location being near the rear of the House of Correction.

Little is known about this manufactory operated by S. T. & G. Bowler in 1851 apart from the fact that it had several ownerships; produced muslins at one period; had 250 looms at work in March 1862; and shortly after appearing in the 1880

33

Trade Directory with Cato Street for its address, left the Preston lists.

On 27 July 1846 an Act of Incorporation had been passed to allow the Fleetwood, Preston and West Riding Junction Railway to purchase the Preston and Longridge line, the intention being to connect both lines in Preston, then extend the Longridge line from Grimsargh eastward into the West Riding. The plan failed to materialise except for the connecting line in Preston between the Maudland and Deepdale stations, the line opening in 1850 to run underground in places and creating a new station in Deepdale, named Deepdale Bridge. The old line from this point to the original Deepdale terminus became a siding for goods and coal. Stone supplies from the Longridge quarries were also stored in this area, and it would be in anticipation of these sidings that the first phase of mills for the New Preston district would be planned for the fifties.

Peel Mill in Fletcher Road was one of the first, erected in 1850 with a fourth floor added to the mill block in the following year when the factory appeared in the Trade Directory for Messrs Napier & Goodair, cotton spinners and manufacturers, who also ran Brookfield Mill at this time. Peel Mill was often referred to as Peel Hall Mill on account of it having been built on the site of Peel Hall shown on the 1840s map. During the 1890s, Peel Mill had two separate main engine plants; one being a single cylinder beam with pusher, the other a single McNaughted beam. The latter engine could hardly run its machinery and because the high pressure cylinder was indicating a mere 85 horsepower in comparison to the 189 horsepower being generated within the low pressure cylinder at 32 rpm, clearly the high pressure side of the engine was in dire need of repair. Bore diameters were 33″ and 38″ on respective strokes of 2′ 9″ and 5′ 6″; corresponding average steam pressures being 56 and 10 psi.

The combined single beam and pusher were also running at 32rpm, the beam engine with a 40″ cylinder bore × 6′ stroke, indicating 189 horsepower on an average steam pressure of 13 psi. As for the horizontal pusher engine, which most likely was in an adjacent engine room and coupled to the beam engine by an extended crankshaft, 486 horsepower was being indicated on an average steam pressure of 76 psi. This latter figure was a good working pressure and therefore an indication that this engine of 26″ cylinder bore × 6′ stroke had been of recent arrival.

In close proximity to Peel Mill, five more textile businesses would appear: Wellington and Deepdale Mills in Deepdale Mill Street; Victoria Mills in Peel Hall Street; Lutwidge Mill in Isherwood Street; and Alexandra Mill in Skeffington Road.

18. A plan of Ribbleton Mill, 1897.

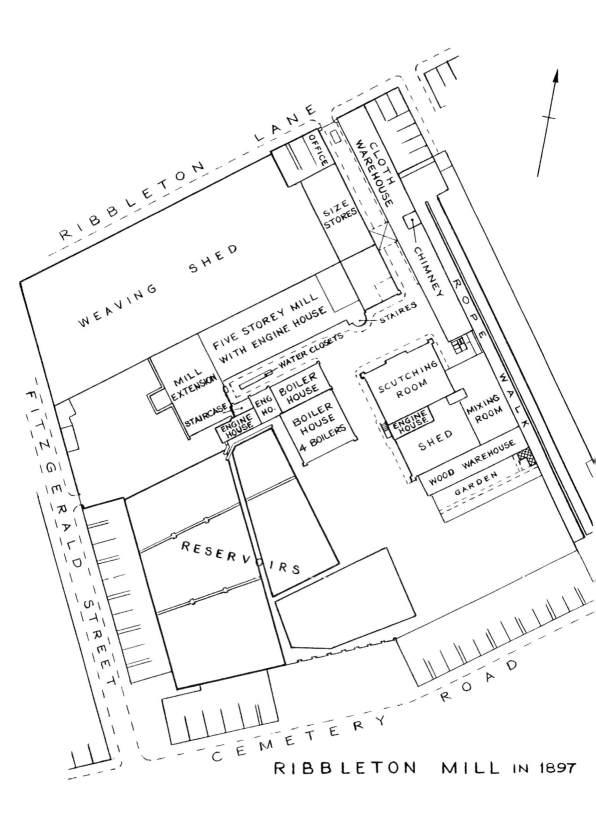

RIBBLETON LANE

OFFICE

CLOTH WAREHOUSE

SIZE STORES

WEAVING SHED

CHIMNEY

ROPE

FIVE STOREY MILL WITH ENGINE HOUSE

STAIRES

WATER CLOSETS

MILL EXTENSION

STAIRCASE

ENG. HO.

BOILER HOUSE

SCUTCHING ROOM

WALK

ENGINE HOUSE

ENGINE HOUSE

BOILER HOUSE 4 BOILERS

SHED

MIXING ROOM

WOOD WAREHOUSE

GARDEN

FITZGERALD STREET

RESERVOIRS

ROAD

CEMETERY

RIBBLETON MILL IN 1897

The year 1850 saw the building of Ribbleton Mill at the corner of what would become Fitzgerald Street and Ribbleton Lane, the mill being the 'combined' factory of J. & H. Seed in 1855. Its engine layout during the 1890s was an interesting one consisting of a double McNaughted beam coupled to a horizontal compound pusher; in all six cylinders producing an aggregate of 840 ihp.

In the description for the combined engines, the term 'pusher' was not mentioned but simply indicated that the horizontal engine had been added in 1869 and was coupled to the beam engine. The pair of beam engines had identical bores of 28″ and 31″, one set of cylinders indicating 95 and 119 ihps, the other set indicating 79 and 130 ihps; whilst the pusher with 22″ and 32″ bores was generating 116 and 189 ihps. As to the pusher engine this would have been in the form of a single tandem with high and low pressure cylinders in tandem sharing the same piston rod, or a side by side compound with the two cylinders adjacent to one another. This latter version of the horizontal compound engine was limited to smaller powers, but its narrow dimensions like those of the single tandem, could be an advantage in a pusher arrangement.

19. Ribbleton Mill with its large area of condenser reservoirs. Near the bottom right of the photograph are the shed and condenser reservoirs of nearby Albert Mill.

Mid-century Developments

20. 'Saddle' at the top of a column in Manchester Mill. This enabled the loading on the column on the floor above to be transferred to the column shown here without crushing the wooden beam. Saddles also gave the whole structure some rigidity.

Before the twentieth century, the term 'side by side' was commonly used by engine makers to describe an entirely different version of the horizontal engine; – the cross compound whose high and low pressure cylinders were positioned wide apart, with a crank on either side of the drive wheel. In the Preston Union Valuations of 1896–97 the descriptions 'cross compound' and 'side by side' were never used, only 'horizontal tandem', 'compound horizontal', or in some instances 'horizontal'. So with the exception of 'horizontal tandem' the brief terminology used for some horizontal engines in the Preston Valuations makes it impossible to ascertain the precise cylinder arrangement.

At Ribbleton, mills 1 and 2 contained 9,712 spindles for twist (thread for the beam of a loom); 10,058 for weft (thread for the shuttle); and 9,856 on throstles. A total of 741 looms were operating, and for the scutching room there was another horizontal engine. This 20 horsepower engine with a 25″ bore × 3′ 6″ stroke had also been made in 1869 as had the mill's machinery and four boilers, each 7′ dia × 28′ in length which were steaming at 75 psi.

Therefore in 1869 the mill had undergone a major refurbishment in machinery and power plant, when most likely the original beam engines of 1850 were McNaughted; a refurbishment which followed a major structural collapse of a mill block on 20 March 1866, when the factory had just recommenced work after a period of idleness due to the Cotton Famine.

A report in the *Preston Guardian* of 21 March describing the collapse said that it was the building at the north east corner of the site, a four-storey block built upon the fireproof principle and one which would have had cast-iron beams and brick arches, which was seen as the possible cause of the collapse. On the ground floor was the boiler house with three boilers, then came the scutching department on the first floor followed by the two upper remaining floors which had been allocated for further preparation processes.

A graphic description of the collapse stated: 'Without a crack or noise of any sort – in fact without the least possible warning – the entire building in this particular direction fell, in one tremendous crash, to the very basement.' The collapse was utter and complete, nothing remaining but 'the white-washed squares at the sides of the contiguous portions of the mill'.

The first half of the nineteenth century found many structural engineers with only a limited knowledge of cast-iron beam design and the mechanics of transverse strain, reverting to the established methods of 'comparative design'; a rather rule of thumb approach. Engineering books of the day presented only simple rules and design tables, and even though engineers such as Eaton Hodgkinson and William Fairbairn would present valuable data on the behaviour of cast iron under load, confidence in the use of this metal in certain areas of buildings would remain debatable to well after mid-century.

One problem in a fireproof building could be the brick arches for the floors, not having been built with sufficient rise at their centres. This could result in the sinking of the arches thus placing additional stresses on adjacent cast-iron beams, resulting in their failure to bear the load, and the overall collapse of the structure. This may well have been the case at Ribbleton Mill, its collapse seemingly being a classic example of cast-iron beam failure.

Moon's Mill in Higher Walton on the outskirts of Preston was the scene of building activity in 1850 when a large multi-storey spinning block was erected. This was in addition to a cotton factory which in 1823, when water-powered, had belonged to James Livesey who is listed in the Preston Trade Directory for 1828 as a cotton manufacturer. The old mill had replaced an earlier cotton factory burnt down in 1811 which had originally been a corn mill owned by Thomas Livesey in 1790 and occupied by Robert Hilton of Preston in 1792, before its conversion into a cotton mill by Messrs Salisbury & Company in the early 1800s.

In 1851 the Higher Walton site was supporting two separate businesses; one belonging to Thomas Livesey who was cotton spinning in the old mill, and one associated with the Rodgett brothers who were cotton spinning and weaving in their new mill, having started up in the enterprise with the help of their father, Miles Rodgett of Bow Lane Mill, Preston.

From the outset, the new Higher Walton factory was engined

21. Spinning mules at Horrocks' Yard Works. The photograph shows the brick arch ceiling construction. (*Harris Museum, Preston*)

by a pair of single cylinder low pressure beam engines, their McNaughting coming later in the 1870s by W. & J. Yates of Blackburn. Five boilers were to be made in 1875–76 by Stevensons of Preston in preparation for the compounding which was carried out in the following year. By this date the mill had undergone a change in ownership, an entry for 1877 in W. & J. Yates's Book of Engine Lists (1876–84) recording the McNaughting of a pair of beam engines for G. & R. Dewhurst at Higher Walton. Each engine was to have a high pressure cylinder bore of 38″ × 3′ 6″ stroke, and a low pressure cylinder bore of 44⅜″ × 7′ stroke. Fitted with McNaught & Varley's patent cut off valves, the engines were still at work in the 1890s, running at 24¼ rpm to drive a shed; average pressure in each high pressure cylinder being 30 psi, and a figure of 8 psi for each low pressure cylinder.

In 1860 another mill block, complete with chimney, boiler house, engine house and water tower was built end-on to the 1850 block to present an impressive profile to the Higher Walton site. The engines for the 1860 factory, which presumably began work as a pair of single cylinder beam engines, were running in a McNaughted form in the 1890s, when they were driving mills '3 & 4'; a reference being made to Hicks of Bolton. The high pressure cylinder bores were identical in both engines as were the low pressure ones at 38″ and 50″ respectively; the three-storey high engine house being 70′ 6″ in length × 34′ 9″ in width.

On a visit during the 1970s to the internal engine room of the 1850s block I found evidence of the double beam engine by way of some ceiling metalwork and the exquisite ironwork stairing which remained in situ. Outside, the mill's tall, square chimney complete with oversailer, stood high in the Higher Walton skyline, a survivor of the mill era unlike the chimney of the 1860s mill which went in 1937.

In Preston, Southgate Mill next to Brookfield Mill off North Road, was a spinning and weaving factory opened in 1851 for James Naylor. In the 1890s, having been under the ownership of Joseph Smith for many years, Southgate was still a combined concern, the mill side being driven by a single McNaughted beam engine of 31″ and 38″ bores, and the weaving section powered by a horizontal compound of 15″ and 20″ bores. The boiler plant was consuming 60 tons of coal per week and offering a steam pressure of 80 psi. This latter figure is a good indicator that the horizontal engine and boiler plant probably arrived in the previous decade or were of most recent arrival.

Another newcomer to the Preston scene in 1851 was Meadow Street Mill for Edward Edge, near the corner of Stanleyfield Road and Meadow Street. This tiny manufactory was known as St Paul's Road Mill in 1855, and in 1860 was in the ownership of

22. Weaving shed, St Paul's Road Mill, on electric drive. (*Harris Museum, Preston*)

John Hawkins. In the nineties classification the only engine data listed was a figure of 25 horsepower which referred to the power available to the machinery.

A short distance from Meadow Street Mill in 1851 was Isaac Simpson's Cottage Street Mill which is shown on the 1844–47 Ordnance Survey Map bounded by Derby Street, Cottage Street, and Pole Street. Derby Street incidentally had been the business address of J. A. Turner & Co., hand loom weavers in 1841 and still there in 1855.

The Cottage Street factory was operating for Thomas Blackhurst and Co. in 1855, and in 1862 contained 16,608 spindles. By the end of the sixties it was listed for Montague B. Copland, under whose name it went during the nineties as Pole Street Mill when it had a single cylinder beam engine of 35¾″ bore × 6′ stroke coupled to a horizontal pusher of 21½″ bore × 6′ stroke, the combination running at 35½ rpm. Two boilers had been made in 1872 to steam at 75 psi, the same year when a new block had been built, so the pusher must have arrived then.

In 1951 when plastic makers Attwater & Sons Ltd had long been the occupiers of the factory, the old engine house with its 9′ 2″ wide chamber rising four storeys was still facing Cottage Street. At the time an old employee recalled how as a boy he often watched from the street the governor balls whirling round and the piston (which would have been the piston rod or the connecting rod of the beam engine) heaving up and down.

In 1851 Parker Street Mill near Brookhouse Mill was a new spinning factory for Simpson & Johnson and by 1855 it had passed into the ownership of Joseph and John Haslam. On 9 March 1860 at about six o'clock in the morning the mill burned down. In that year a new engine house was erected, presumably either for a new engine or the original one which, if it had escaped fire damage, would be in a good condition assuming it was new around 1851.

The factory is absent from the list of cotton mills for March 1862, but is in production in 1865. In the 1890s its engine is recorded as a horizontal compound of 26″ and 40¼″ bores × 6′ stroke; respective indicated horsepowers being 242 and 188. Power available to the machinery, which included 18,576 spindles for twist and 22,728 for weft, was 140 horsepower, and the bore dimensions of the engine are a fair indication that it was of the cross compound type. Claytons made three boilers in 1879 for 80 psi pressure and in 1888 the engine received new cylinders.

In the 1950s Parker Street Mill was a tannery for the Ribble Leather Company before its demolition. Facing the Parker Street entrance stood the engine house with its 1860 datestone, alongside the boiler house behind which was the new mill block of 1860. To the west lay the reservoirs and some distance away on the Eldon Street boundary was the large square chimney. There is a story that when the chimney was about to be felled, bricks were removed from its base and wooden supports inserted in readiness for burning. Overnight a strong wind got up and the inevitable happened; early morning light revealed a pile of rubble.

Nearby in what would be Maynard Street, Bold Street Mill was raised upon land which like Parker Street had been green fields at the time of the 1844–47 Ordnance Survey. The Bold Street factory was listed for spinning in 1855 for J. T. Blackhurst & Co., and as a manufactory for Thomas Maynard in 1860. M. S. Maynard was operating self-acting mules two years later at the mill where, in the early 1880s, 130 hands were in employment.

It was probably in the eighties or late seventies that the original steam engine at Bold Street Mill was replaced by the horizontal engine at work in the 1890s which had 25″ and 43″ bores × 5′ stroke; the bore sizes leading one to suggest that it was most probably a cross compound. For 50 rpm, the high pressure cylinder was indicating 210 horsepower and the low pressure a figure of 310; not a well-balanced engine but one offering 138 horsepower to the machinery. Three boilers, one made of steel and two of iron, were providing a steam pressure of 80 psi.

Sited alongside the main West Coast railway line, Bold Street Mill remained in the Maynard name until closure in the late 1930s. Parker Street Mill also closed at that time under the M. S. Maynard name with which it had been associated since the mid-1890s.

Two cotton factories erected in close proximity to one another in the early 1850s, alongside Greenbank Street and near McGuffog's Mill, were Richard Goodair's Springfield Mill which was a manufactory, and Daniel Arkwright's Arkwright Mill which operated as a combined spinning and weaving factory; both establishments had their reservoirs sited alongside Brook Street.

Springfield Mill, bounded by Murray Street to the south and Aqueduct Street to the north, was absent from the town map of 1852 but listed for Goodair in 1855. In 1862, the manufactory had 530 looms, and in 1890 Stevensons made two boilers for 90 psi pressure which was probably the time when the horizontal compound engine running in the 1890s with 22″ and 36″ bores × 6′ stroke, was fitted as a replacement engine under a modernisation and expansion programme. Up to about 1890 the layout of buildings had been limited to the north western area alongside Greenbank Street and Aqueduct Street. However, new weaving facilities were added on the Brook Street side; the 1890s

Classification indicated that there would be 1,122 looms when all filled, with about 86 ordinary looms not yet in. The engine was developing 373 ihp in its high pressure cylinder and 143 ihp in its low pressure one, and horsepower on offer to the machinery amounted to 106.

Arkwright Mill was erected in 1853 and fitted with a pair of low pressure beam engines, McNaughting most likely taking place in 1880 when Claytons made five boilers to steam at 70 psi pressure. Both engines had identical bores of 38″ and 42″, and an engine test in July 1896 showed average working pressures in one engine to be 30 psi for the high pressure cylinder and 11 psi for the low pressure one, to develop 196 and 177 ihp respectively, whilst figures for the second engine were 33.5 and 9.5 psi developing respective ihps of 216 and 158.

At this time, Arkwright had 20,064 spindles for twist, 16,184 for weft, and 599 looms. With 184 horsepower on offer to machinery requiring 189, the engines were certainly loaded from the effect of what must have been a heavy geared drive and transmission system. Such a system operated to well into the First World War until the engines were replaced.

Stourton Mill in George Street, off London Road in the Lark Hill area, was a recently built spinning factory for Eastham Brothers in 1855. In 1869 under George Eastham the mill was closed, most likely due to the after-effects of the Famine. By the early 1870s, it was back in production for Mellor Brothers who still owned the mill in the nineties when it was being driven by a single cylinder beam engine and pusher.

The description of the engine in the Classification for Assessment Purposes of 1896–97, simply states 'beam', but an examination of the general statistics given indicates a beam and pusher arrangement. Cylinder bore diameter and stroke respectively for the beam engine are recorded as 42″ and 6′, whilst those of the pusher engine as 22¼″ and again the same stroke of 6′, engine revolutions for the combination being 33 rpm. The boiler pressure of 90 psi from the two boilers also indicate a recent installation of steam raising plant for what must have been an engine modification and the arrival of a horizontal pusher engine. Power available to the machinery was 124 horsepower of which 106 was required, so it was an engine seemingly performing well in its daily work. In the mechanic's shop a vertical engine of 7″ bore × 12″ stroke was running at 45 rpm to offer 3 horsepower.

In the mid-1850s, very little hand loom weaving was surviving in Preston, but in 1855 a three-storey building, about twenty-five yards long, was erected for this particular trade off New Hall

Lane for James Birch Williamson. Reference to the building was in a report in the *Preston Guardian* of 23 June 1875, which mentions the destruction, presumably by fire, of New Hall Lane Mill belonging to Messrs Emery and Dyson. The report stated:

> The Mill is situated about midway up New Hall Lane. It fronts Mr Brindle's Mill, and is on the west side of the large manufactory of Messrs Calverts.
>
> The structure is generally known by the name of Williamson's shop – built in 1855, and was for some time used for hand loom weaving.

Brindle's Mill referred to in the report was Alliance Works, and a visit to the mill in January 1992 found documents relating to the beginnings of the mill and a mention of Williamson who had been manufacturing in 1855 at Back Lane and Moor Lane Mills. In 1860 at the New Hall Lane site, Williamson had wanted to straighten a land boundary line, presumably with the intention of building. By 1862 he had erected premises and was having to pay The London Insurance a premium of £14.11s. 9d., on the understanding that there was to be no carding or spinning, only weaving, on the premises which would be situated opposite his mill building of 1855. In 1862, Williamson was operating 532 looms, six days per week in the new Alliance Mill, then presumably under steam power, according to the *Preston Chronicle* of 12 March. The manufactory is represented by J. B. Williamson & Co. in 1865, and listed as J. B. Williamson & Son (executors of) Alliance Mills, New Hall Lane, in the 1869 Directory.

One of the papers examined at the mill referred to 5 July 1872, when an Agreement was made between Thomas Brindle and George Frederick Hinshelwood, both of Preston, and John Emery of Manchester. Part of the Agreement mentions: 'Hand Loom Weaving warehouse three stories high ... and other outbuilding now standing'. Further on it reads: '... erect and complete on the said premises a Steam Engine in substitution of the one now erected on the premises of sufficient horsepower to work Eighty power looms and preparations and shall also provide and fit up shafting for the same Engine'.

Alliance was under the new ownership of T. Brindle & Company in 1873, and the new engine mentioned was to be a horizontal compound made by Wood of Bolton in 1872. In April 1896 it was developing 288 ihp at 51½rpm, bores being 22″ and 34″ × 4′ 6″ stroke. Two boilers by Clayton were used, and in the sizing room was a tiny relief engine of 8″ bore × 10″ stroke, which would relieve the main engine during the lunchtime break thus ensuring the sizing process was continuous. The 1890s

Mid-century Developments

Classification mentions the old part of the mill having been erected by J. B. Williamson in 1862, and the mill having 1,000 looms in 1879.

By 1856, the huge cotton empire of Horrockses, Miller & Company had ten mills driven by twelve engines, operating 154,334 spindles and 2,775 looms. Over 3,000 hands were in its employment with about 95,000 lbs weight of yarn and 400,000 yards of cloth being produced weekly. In stark contrast the long-established Preston flax trade was in sharp decline with only two mills left in the town, whilst for the cotton industry, four mills were in course of erection or being filled with machinery.

One of these mills was Paul Catterall's 1856 five-storey factory in Rigby Street, off New Hall Lane, known as simply the New Hall Lane Mill. On 1 November 1875, it was the scene of a fire responsible for damages amounting to £26,000, when the spinning block was gutted and eighteen pairs of mules lost. Rebuilding on

23. Plan of Arkwright Mill in 1896–97.

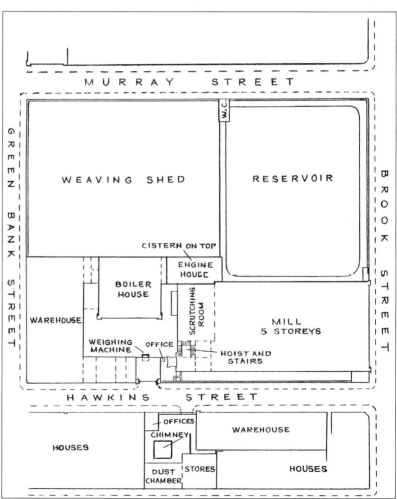

the fireproof principle comprising brick arches, wrought-iron tie rods and iron beams began soon afterwards, with production recommencing in about March 1877.

Under reference DDX189, item 33 in the Lancashire Record Office is an account of the rebuilding work to be undertaken: 'Estimate for the construction of Catterall's Mill, New Hall Lane, Preston', with an incorrect date of 1844, which must have been added later as the figures are not in the same style or hand as the text. Some of the statements in the estimate illustrate the magnitude of damage:

'Take down west gable wall to the set-off in brickwork over Engine House, and also about 10 feet from top of Hoist Tower'; 'Remove such portion, of the outer west gable to suit form of new Roof'; 'Make good all broken slates on Boiler House Roof'; 'Make good Engine House windows where damaged'.

The beam engine which had been made by Clayton in 1856 survived the fire as did its pusher tandem engine which had been fitted by W. & J. Yates of Blackburn in 1872, both engines working on the same crankpin. These engines and their boilers

24. Weaving sheds at the rear of Alliance works. In the distance is Centenary Mill. *(Harris Museum, Preston)*

were for sale by auction on 21 April 1887; this obviously came to nothing because they were still in situ years later, but the sale inventory offered interesting data:

> Boilers –Three by Stevenson & Co., Preston, 1878. 30′ × 7′ 6″, working at 75 lb pressure.
> Engines – Beam Engine (McNaughted), high – 36″ bore × 3′ 6″ stroke, low – 45″ bore × 7′ stroke, 400 ihp. Horizontal tandem, high – 16″, low – 36″ × 7′ stroke, 170 ihp.

The horizontal engine had been thoroughly overhauled by W. & J. Yates in 1883, and in 1876 the same firm had fitted a new high pressure cylinder to the beam engine, the McNaughting modification. In the 1890s, the same engines were driving 28,152 weft spindles and 11,384 throstle spindles. Only two boilers were in use, and bore diameters for the beam engine were given as 36″ and 42″, whilst for the single tandem compound pusher engine, bore diameters of 16″ and 30″ were recorded, the combination running at 29 rpm.

Further along Rigby Street at its junction with Cemetery Road was Albert Mill, a manufactory which had been established in the second half of the 1850s, and listed in the 1857 Directory for Wilcockson, Swarbrick & Jesper at Ribbleton Lane. Following several changes in ownership the mill was under the Barnacre Weaving Co. Ltd in 1898, and in 1895 when new machinery was being put in, the engine was a single McNaughted beam engine with 22″ and 30″ bores with respective strokes of 2′ 6″ and 5′. Average steam pressure in the high pressure cylinder was 35.5 psi, and 6.6 psi in the low pressure cylinder, and corresponding ihps were 59 and 41. One boiler, 7′ diameter and 30′ in length, made by Claytons in 1874, was steaming at 75 psi pressure.

Another new Preston factory, an addition to the 1857 Directory, was Shelley Road Mill near the canal and at the rear of Brookhouse Mill. In 1862, it had 42,112 spindles on 35 pairs of self-acting mules, and two years later it was to have a fine water tower, recently demolished. The mill was first engined with a pair of single cylinder beam engines, probably compounded in 1886 when W. & J. Yates made two steel boilers which in 1896 were part of a bank of four, the other two being the original iron ones. The engines were identical in that each had 33¼″ and 35″ bores on 3′ and 6′ respective strokes, and at 32rpm one was developing 157 and 138 ihps, the other 170 and 112.

Driving the weaving shed was a single cylinder horizontal engine of 36″ bore × 5′ 6″ stroke made locally by John Stevenson, but which had been removed by December 1898. At that time 80 looms had been temporarily removed because of a fire and the

Mid-century Developments

25. The handsome profile of the octagonal chimney at Paul Catterall's New Hall Lane Mill in Maitland Street. Erected with its mill in 1856, it is seen here standing near the spinning block which was gutted in a fire of 1875.

26. 'Fireproof' construction of iron beams and brick arches in the new-built spinning block of New Hall Lane Mill.

number of spindles in the mill amounted to 10,920 for twist and 12,600 for weft. In 1857 the factory was listed under cotton spinners for James Threlfall & Son and the same in 1869, before a change in status to a combined concern under the same ownership by 1873, when the Stevenson horizontal had probably arrived.

Croft Street Mill appeared in the Trade Directory for 1857 as the new mill of T. C. Hincksman & Co., the spinning factory served by a railway branch line. It would begin production with a pair of single cylinder beam engines to be compounded later, possibly in 1876 when Stevensons made three boilers for 80 psi pressure. In 1896 each engine had 28″ and 32″ bores on respective strokes of 3′ and 6′, and at 33 rpm were driving 36,912 spindles on 23 pairs of mules. The factory had no reservoir but relied instead on the canal some distance away for condenser feed.

By 1857 a second manufactory had appeared in St Paul's Road, listed in the Trade Directory for Lancaster & Brother. It would be known as Astley Field Mill and was situated between St Barnabas's Place and Astley Street, John Lancaster having 320 looms there in 1862. The single cylinder beam engine at work in the nineties at Astley Field for Hopkins & Martin must have been the original engine to be pusher-compounded at a later date.

Acting as the low pressure engine in the combination, the beam engine had a 20½″ bore × 4′ 6″ stroke whilst the high pressure horizontal pusher worked on a 16″ bore × 3′ 2″ stroke. This engine arrangement was running at 50 rpm, with one boiler for 80 psi pressure in attendance made by Yates & Thom of Blackburn.

William Thom, the Works manager of the Blackburn firm, had become a partner in 1885, so it would seem that the boiler had recently arrived at Astley Field, presumably for the installation of the pusher engine. An almost perfect balance of power was being met from the two engines working together; 72 ihp in the pusher and 71.2 ihp in the beam engine. Power available for the machinery amounted to 37 horsepower of which 32 was required.

William Yates had started the Blackburn Works with George Parkinson of the Cleaver Street Foundry in about 1835–36, Yates continuing with his sons in the early 1840s when Parkinson left. Engines, boilers, waterwheels, factory gearing and railway wheels were amongst the products to leave the Blackburn Works known as the Canal Foundry. In the 1850s the firm began to specialise in mill engines and millwrighting, coal winders and steam raising plant, for which it became renowned both at home and abroad. William and John Yates continued productivity after their father's death, William Thom eventually becoming a partner. In 1927 lack of orders led to voluntary liquidation, the Preston firm of Joseph Foster & Sons purchasing the Blackburn Works in 1928 which then went under the name of Foster, Yates & Thom. Trade ended in 1973 and during tidying-up operations, two books of engine lists for 1857–76 and 1876–84 were apparently rescued from rubbish and taken into the care of Blackburn Reference Library. These books have been of the utmost value in tracing some Preston engines.

A third mill block was erected at Brookhouse Mills in 1858 to be engined by a single cylinder beam engine made locally by Clayton, later to be pusher-compounded by a single cylinder horizontal engine, again made locally, by Allsup. In 1896–97 the combination was driving the mill, a shed, and a warehouse. The pusher acting as the high pressure engine had a 24⅛″ bore × 7′ stroke and was working on an average steam pressure of 52 psi, whilst the low pressure beam engine had a 39½″ bore × 7′ stroke and was operating on an average pressure of 10 psi; the combination running at 26 rpm.

As the 1850s drew to a close, the growth of the Preston cotton industry was clearly illustrated by the mill listings in the 1860 Trade Directory. Twenty nine firms were in manufacturing only, thirteen in spinning only, and twenty eight in combined spinning

27. Water tower of the 1860s: Shelley Road Mills, near the Lancaster Canal.

28. Beam engine house supporting the boilers' cistern tank at Shelley Road Mills. On the far right is the engine house erected for a horizontal cross compound engine of 1908 (see Chapter 9).

and weaving. Much had been achieved technologically in applying steam power to the power looms and new mules of the town's factories, whose products were meeting the needs of the home and foreign markets.

The new, graceful beam engines at this time epitomised not only the wealth and status of their owners, but also the latest developments of steam power in the factory arena. By 1860, Preston's population had reached 82,000; its cotton industry was still expanding; but soon it would enter one of the darkest and most dramatic periods of its history with the outbreak of the American Civil War and its effects on cotton supplies. When American cotton returned to Lancashire in the mid-1860s, a new era of steam engine technology was under way.

CHAPTER FIVE

The Famine Years and a New Engine

THE DECADE of the 1860s are remembered for the appalling effects the American Civil War of 1861–65 had on the Lancashire cotton industry, in particular on the liveliehoods of its operatives. When Abraham Lincoln became President of the United States in 1860, the southern states began to see their economic standing increasingly subordinated to that of the north, and although the enslavement of Africans on the southern cotton plantations gave the impeding war a moral issue, it was never at the root of it. As war commenced, a blockade of cotton shipments had an immediate effect on the Lancashire industry, but contrary to popular belief the crisis in Lancashire was not entirely due to a shortage of cotton.

In 1860 over three quarters of Lancashire's cotton had arrived from the southern states, and in the previous year more cotton had been produced than was needed. Lancashire manufacturers took advantage of this cheap and plentiful supply as well as a large demand for cotton goods from the Far East by working their mills at high pressure to enjoy two years of almost unexampled prosperity.

By May 1860 the overseas demand had been met and a large supply of cotton goods accumulated, which would have led to loss of profits if the high rate of production had gone on. Many mill owners found themselves weakened by over-extension and in need of working capital, and in one respect the Cotton Famine was to benefit a good many Lancashire manufacturers in that by the autumn of 1862 and the spring of 1863, when cotton goods were in demand, they were able to sell off their stocks at much higher prices than normal. These gains help to explain why bankers showed confidence in the cotton industry about this time, and why during 1863 the construction of mills previously contracted for had been resumed.

In the autumn of 1862 about forty new mills were ready or nearly ready for starting in and around Blackburn when trade revived, and in the following spring in Bolton seven or eight of the largest mills were being built or filling with machinery. In the district of Colne preparations were under way for the addition of 20,000 spindles and 5,325 looms; 1,450 looms in the Padiham district; and 150,000 spindles and 3,600 looms in the Burnley area. Altogether throughout the Lancashire industry, no fewer than 98 united liability cotton companies were formed in 1860–61 and 24 in 1862–65.

In 1860 the consumption of cotton in Great Britain had averaged 51,700 bales of 400 lbs per week. By 1862 the figure had fallen to 21,700 bales and in November only 18,000 bales could be accounted for, affording a little over two days' employment per week for more than half a million operatives; such were the effects of the American blockade.

In Preston the Cotton Famine had set in toward the end of 1861 and would last until nearly mid-1865, years of distress during which thousands of men, women and children received help from the Poor Law Guardians. The most able-bodied men and youths were put to work on stone breaking, earth excavating and levelling, including the cutting of a mill lodge, the construction of sewerage works, road making and the laying out of building plots on the Ribbleton Freehold Estate. The severity of the Famine on the town's cotton industry was reported by the *Preston Chronicle* of 12 March 1862, listing number of mules and looms stopped, and reductions in the working week.

Immediately prior to and during the Famine, cotton factory construction was still very much in evidence in Preston. New Hall Lane Mill near the junction of New Hall Lane and Stanley Street, and Hartford Mill a short distance away in Campbell Street, were erected in 1860, and engined with the traditional beam engine.

The New Hall Lane Mill engine was running at 31 rpm as a single McNaughted version during the 1890s for Eccles Bros, cylinder bores being 20″ and 38″ with corresponding ihps on offer of 120.4 and 168.8. At this time the mill had another engine, a horizontal compound with 18″ and 29½″ bores × 4′ stroke offering corresponding ihps of 99.8 and 94.4 at 51 rpm. Three boilers were steaming at 80 psi pressure, one having been made by Clayton in 1874, the other two by Galloways in 1876. The Green's economiser was two years old, and there was the mention of a flywheel always breaking down.

In 1897, the engine layout for the spinning side of Hartford Mill, which had 41,000 spindles, was described as 'compound beam and hor. pushers 4 cyl.', with two sets of 16″ and 30″ bores being listed. 'Compound beam' was in error and should have read 'combined beams' to indicate a pair of single cylinder beam engines, each pusher compounded by a horizontal engine of 16″ bore.

At Hartford the installation of rope drive had involved the

stoppage of three pairs of mules. Roof timbers were in a bad condition and were being replaced; in fact the mill block roof which at this particular time would be a multi-pitch one, would eventually be replaced by a flat, felt covered one.

The factory also had a horizontal compound engine driving a shed which probably arrived in *c.* 1882 when Hartford was listed as a combined concern. Unfortunately engine data was not listed, but there was the mention that in 1891 Yates & Thom had provided three boilers. At 8′ 6″ in diameter and 30′ in length, these were blowing at 100 psi, coal consumption being 80 tons per week, and this recent modernisation of steam raising plant was most probably for the pusher compounding. A vertical engine of 8″ bore was also in attendance for the size house and mechanics' shop.

On 6 February 1861 John Hawkins & Sons' Greenbank Mill was totally destroyed by fire, damages amounting to between

29. Mills in the New Hall Lane area. Hartford Mill is seen in the centre, while bottom centre is Alliance Works, to the right of which is India Mill, then Manchester Mill. Bottom left are the reservoir pens of New Preston Mills.

30. John Hawkins & Sons'
Greenbank Mill, illustrating a
'combined mill' site of
multi-storey blocks and weaving
sheds. At the bottom is the
reservoir wall on the Adelphi
Street brow; the second
reservoir is at the top left corner
alongside Moor Brook Street.
A little further on are the sheds
and spinning block of Moor
Brook Mill.

£25,000 and £30,000. Following the rebuilding programme, the town map of 1865 shows a much larger factory layout with the addition of mill blocks and another reservoir, the latter sited alongside Moor Brook Street, and the original reservoir adjacent to the Adelphi Street brow having been retained. The fire had been in a five-storey block standing in a north-south alignment at the north end of the site. During the rebuilding period, two blocks were erected in 1862 on the fireproof principle, one to face Gordon Street on the southern side of the site, the other to the north. To complete the new factory complex a giant of a square chimney appeared, recorded in the nineties as 80 yards in height with a base side of 20 feet, the tallest in Preston at that time. It was also probably the last of the square types to be erected in Preston, its construction taking place when circular chimneys were about to make their debut on the town's skyline.

The 1890s Classification only offered horsepower ratings for Greenbank Mills; 250 for Mill 1 and 250 for Mill 2 (winding), although there is mention of a pumping engine and a horizontal engine. What is known is that in 1938, three beam engines were still in situ at Greenbank which were replaced by electric motor drive. Greenbank was a combined establishment before and after the fire of 1861. It had 950 looms in 1862 and 1,628 in the early

1880s when the 'New Mill' contained 24 pairs of mules; the 'Old Mill', 6 pairs; and the Gordon Street block, 6 pairs. No information has been found to say whether a horizontal engine installation for weaving was ever part of the rebuilding programme of the 1860s.

It was not until the late 1850s that Lancashire engine builders began to take a serious interest in the horizontal engine for textile mill drive, even though it had been used in various fields of industry in Britain and America before this time. Certainly by the early 1860s, Lancashire engine firms were building horizontal engines for weaving shed drive at a time when the beam engine was still looked upon as the prime mover for high power ratings allied to spinning and its preparatory processes.

William Yates of Blackburn, for example, had begun to build horizontal engines in *c.* 1858. The firm provided a single cylinder version in 1861 for Navigation Mills, Blackburn; one in 1862 for another Blackburn mill; and a compound version in 1865 destined for Bombay.

Yet for the Preston and District industry during the 1860s, when a number of new weaving firms were established, there is no firm evidence of a horizontal engine installation in any of these new manufactories. The earliest recorded date for the installation of a horizontal engine is in 1869 at Ribbleton Mill, for the two engines mentioned earlier in Chapter 4. The next date is 1870 for a Yates's horizontal compound engine with 21″ and 36″ bores × 4′ stroke installed at the mill of Messrs Orr & Company, in nearby Bamber Bridge, which in that year also received a compound beam engine from the same Blackburn firm, followed by another horizontal compound engine of 10″ and 18″ bores × 3′ stroke in 1871.

However, what is known for certain is that some of the new manufactories of the 1860s in Preston did open with beam engine drive. Queen's Mill of 1861, on the corner of Greenbank Street and Ripon Street, began operating with a beam engine which was still in service in 1896 driving 750 looms, albeit with the aid of a single cylinder horizontal pusher. The combination was running at 37½ rpm on strokes of 5′, and an engine test in August of that year showed the pusher, which had a 19¾″ bore, developing 110 ihp, whilst the single cylinder beam engine of 38″ bore was achieving 60 ihp.

Although two boilers were in attendance consuming 90 tons of coal per week at Queen's Mill, there were three boilers actually in situ, a strong indicator that the manufactory had been built originally not just for weaving, but spinning too. Clarification of this was found in the 1869 Trade Directory which lists the mill

The Famine Years and a New Engine

under Cotton Spinners and Manufacturers, R. & W. Jackson being the assignees, but what happened at Queen's between 1861 and 1869 is not abundantly clear.

In 1862, R. & W. Jackson are operating 270 looms from a total of 850, three and a half days per week, presumably at Queen's, but in 1865 the two entrepreneurs are listed under Cotton Spinners and Manufacturers, their address being Parker Street. Either they were still at Queen's by this date, when the address would be in error, or they were using premises at Parker Street Mill, Queen's being closed because of the Famine. Perhaps spinning machinery never arrived at Queen's because of the economic instability brought on by the Cotton Famine, but a four-storey block was erected, possibly the intended spinning block, alongside Greenbank Street. Reservoirs were in Ripon Street, and to the north of them, across the mill yard, was the engine house and boiler house and behind them the weaving shed. At the western boundary stood the square chimney, which like the one at Greenbank Mill was amongst the last of its type to be erected in Preston.

Adding to this final batch of square chimneys was the giant with 18′ 6″ base sides built for the New Preston Mill of 1861 for Horrockses, Miller & Company, at the town end of New Hall Lane. Recorded in the 1890s as a 63-yarder, it still survives today minus about twenty feet, removed in 1978. Today, the passerby might be forgiven for assuming that it had been erected for Centenary Mill which stands alongside it, but Centenary once had its own impressive chimney, a circular one at the entrance to the mill yard.

The large 'fireproof' spinning block of New Preston Mill was set well back from New Hall Lane, at the bottom of Bread Street. Behind, backing onto Campbell Street, was its weaving shed, and in March 1862 the mill list in the *Preston Chronicle* discloses that Horrockses, Miller & Company had a 'New Mill' with 1,000 looms, which would be the new Preston factory. At one time the mill had a gas holder with a capacity of 36,000 cubic feet, and a boiler house said to have had seven boilers, steam engine plant of some proportion, which was supported by a large area of condenser pens.

However, as with all the Preston mills belonging to Horrockses, Crewdson & Co. Ltd in the 1890s, very little engine data was recorded in the 1890s Classification for New Preston Mill except the mention of a 350 horsepower beam engine and a 150 horsepower horizontal engine.

A new weaving establishment of the early 1860s was Moor Hall Mill. Although absent from the 1860 Trade Directory it is shown on the 1865 map, somewhat isolated on the northern outskirts, in Brook Street. Ripon Street, a little to the south, was not fully developed and was at the northern extremity of a new mill housing estate on which building had taken place over recent years.

The Trade Directory of 1865 did not list the names of the manufactories, only the names of their proprietors and addresses. Two manufactories in Brook Street were mentioned; Richard Goodair's Springfield Mill, and Hague & Penny's Moor Hall Mill, Brook Street North, where in 1862 only 150 out of a total of 250 looms were working four days a week.

Moor Hall Mill had probably opened in that year or the previous one with a single cylinder beam engine which was still providing motive power in 1897, by which time it had long been pusher-compounded, probably in 1878 when Claytons made the mill's number two boiler for a steam pressure of 80 psi. The pusher had a 20 $\frac{3}{16}$″ bore and at 33 rpm was indicating 124 horsepower, whilst the low pressure beam engine which had a 36 $\frac{3}{16}$″ cylinder bore was achieving 107 ihp. Loomage was made up of 100 Jacquards and 584 Dobbies, all 'fancy' looms which produced intricate patterned cloths.

Hague & Penny are not listed in the 1869 Trade Directory and with no indication whatsoever that the manufactory was operational, it is assumed that it was still closed following the Famine, as were a number of Preston mills at this time including Moor Brook, Southgate, Bow Lane, Oxheys in Ripon Street, the Fylde Road Mill of J. Clayton & Sons, Derby Street Mill, Lord Street Mill, Dale Street Mill, and Stourton Mill.

By 1873, Moor Hall Mill is listed for Edward Healey who was to have a long association with the manufactory, the Healey name still representing it in 1898 by which time it had become a limited concern. Up to at least 1917 the manufactory went under the Healey name but by Guild Year 1922, Holden Bros & Martin Ltd were the proprietors, advertising as 'manufacturers of fancy goods' including 'dhooties, crimps, muslins, lenos, coloured and dress goods etc'. Holden Bros & Martin were still the owners in 1932 before the firm went into closure, a victim of the Depression.

Primrose, or Primrose Hill Mill as it was sometimes referred to, was a new manufactory of the early 1860s, sited on the east side of London Road at the rear of Fishwick Mills. The manufactory is not in the Trade Directory for 1860 but must have opened soon afterwards. Although it is not mentioned by name in the March list of 1862 there is a reference to a Wilkinson having 200 looms, 50 of which were stopped in what must have been the new Primrose Mill because in 1865 Huntington & Wilkinson were manufacturing there.

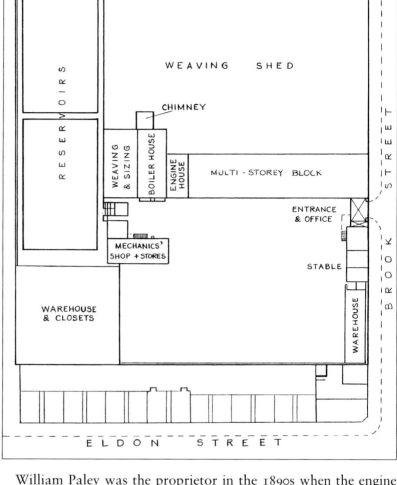

WEAVING SHED

RESERVOIRS

CHIMNEY

WEAVING & SIZING

BOILER HOUSE

ENGINE HOUSE

MULTI - STOREY BLOCK

STREET

ENTRANCE & OFFICE

MECHANICS' SHOP + STORES

STABLE

BROOK

WAREHOUSE & CLOSETS

WAREHOUSE

ELDON STREET

31. A plan of Moor Hall Mill in the 1890s.

William Paley was the proprietor in the 1890s when the engine was recorded as a single cylinder horizontal of 16″ bore × 3′ stroke, indicating 67 ihp at 65½ rpm. At this time a similar engine, although slightly smaller, was running at Hopwood Street Mill, another Paley establishment and where in c. 1886–87 a boiler for 80 psi pressure had been installed. Therefore it is most likely that both engines arrived for a major power plant refurbishment during the eighties for Paley, each replacing a beam engine drive.

In 1904 Primrose was operating under Burton & Frost, continuing under the same partnership until at least 1917, with closure coming sometime between then and 1922. Today, a date of 1907 on its multi-storey block probably bears testimony to the time when steel beams were fitted on its top floor and the construction of a Mansard type roof was undertaken.

Hopwood Street Mill on the corner of Hopwood Street and South Meadow Street, although not listed in 1844, is shown on the 1844–47 Ordnance Survey Map and was operating as a manufactory in 1851. In 1855 Ralph Worden was at Hopwood Street and by 1857 a second weaving business, headed by William Preston, was also in residence; both entrepreneurs still in business in 1860 but apparently not so in March 1862. Their absence from the Trade Directories of 1865 and 1869 leads one to conclude that both fell victim to the Famine, the Hopwood Street manufactory eventually coming under Paley control.

The Hopwood Street engine, a single cylinder horizontal, was the smallest of the main drive engines listed in the 1890s Classification. With a 15″ bore × 2′ 6″ stroke it was generating 60 ihp at 72 rpm; 20 horsepower being available to the machinery which required a mere 14 horsepower. In attendance was a ten year old boiler, and at that time the manufactory had 212 dobbies.

Caledonian Mill in Ribble Street, off the bottom of Pitt Street, was a new manufactory on the town map for 1865. It is not mentioned by name in the directories of 1865 and 1869 but is listed for Leigh & Esplin in 1873, and for John Smalley & Sons in 1877. By the mid-1880s William Entwistle's sons were operating the manufactory and were to continue for some years afterwards before the premises became the weaving establishment of the Caledonian Mill Co. Ltd soon after 1901. In the second half of the 1920s the same company was still operating at Caledonian but by 1932 it would seem that the Charles Manufacturing Company had taken over the business which came to an end soon afterwards.

The engine driving 434 looms at Caledonian in the 1890s was an unusual one for textile mill drive in that it had two identical horizontal cylinders of 18″ bore × 2′ 11″ stroke, each one being a high pressure engine in what must have been a cylinder layout similar to a cross compound arrangement. At 42 rpm, the engine was offering 60 horsepower to machinery requiring 30 horsepower; actual power being taken amounting to 45 horsepower.

A statement in the 1890s Classification clarifies what type of engine it was: 'It is supposed that this engine was formerly a marine one'. Therefore, there is no doubt that it was a type used in sternwheeler and quarterwheeler paddle steamers, and near Caledonian Mill was the marine connection; the foundry of Watson & Allsup who are listed in the Trade Directories of 1851 and 1855 as iron and brass founders of Caledonia Foundry, Lower Pitt Street. Allsup was originally an engineer and millwright in the cotton trade but 'on seeing it going down', as he once said, he entered the shipbuilding business, William Allsup & Sons becoming a well-known Preston firm of shipbuilders.

What with his shipbuilding connection and the immediate

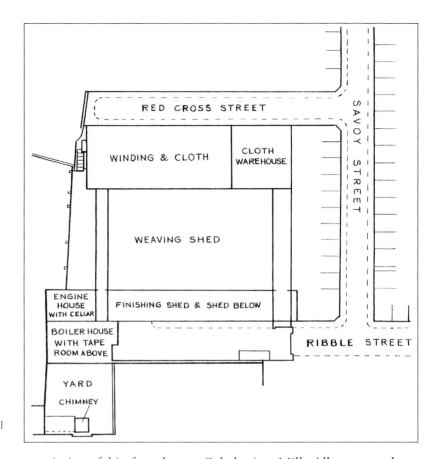

RED CROSS STREET

SAVOY STREET

WINDING & CLOTH

CLOTH WAREHOUSE

WEAVING SHED

ENGINE HOUSE WITH CELLAR

FINISHING SHED & SHED BELOW

BOILER HOUSE WITH TAPE ROOM ABOVE

RIBBLE STREET

YARD

CHIMNEY

32. A plan of Caledonian Mill in the 1890s.

proximity of his foundry to Caledonian Mill, Allsup must have had some influence on the choice of engine for the mill. The word 'formerly' in the Classification statement points to the engine being a second-hand one. However, there is no indication as to who made it and when it arrived at Caledonian, or if it replaced an engine at the mill, only that in the 1890s it was being attended by a steel boiler, 8 feet in diameter and 30 feet 6 inches in length which had been made by Yates to steam at 70 psi pressure.

In 1864, two more cotton factories appeared on the Preston scene; India Mill, a combined establishment for William Calvert, and Manchester Mill, a manufactory for H. C. Outram & Company. Built in close proximity to one another, just off New Hall Lane on its northern side, the mills were operational by 1865.

Hewitson in his 1883 *History of Preston* refers to India Mill as being the last new mill to be built in Preston for some time. In fact, it would be almost thirty years from the building of India Mill before the next new spinning mill would be erected in Preston, the Centenary Mill.

The 1890s Classification lists for India Mill a large horizontal compound engine which must have been of the cross compound type due to the large bores which were 30″ and 52″ × 6′ stroke and no mention of a tandem engine. Running at 36 rpm, the engine was driving 13,788 spindles for twist, 16,440 for weft, and 594 looms. Results of an engine test in 1896 show a well-balanced engine with 310 ihp in the high pressure cylinder and 300 ihp in the low pressure one; respective average steam pressures being 33 psi and 11 psi.

Although four boilers were in situ, only three were working to steam at 75 psi pressure, coal consumption being 58 tons per week. These had been made by Stevenson in 1877 for what might possibly had been the McNaughting of a pair of single cylinder beam engines. As for the year of installation for the horizontal engine, an early 1880s date is likely judging from the similarities in general statistics of two other compound horizontal engines, albeit tandems, belonging to William Calvert in the 1890s; one at his Flats Mills in Walton-le-Dale, and the other tandem engine running at Aqueduct Street Mill. Both tandems had been made in the early 1880s by John Musgrave & Sons of Bolton, so there is the distinct possibility that India's engine arrived during this period from the Bolton works. In 1882–83 William Calvert & Sons had the highest spindleage in the Preston District with 151,146 spindles, and with 2,544 looms were second only to Horrockses, Miller and Co.

At Manchester Mill in the 1890s, the engine there was also a horizontal compound, again presumably a cross compound type, which had 24¼″ and 40¼″ bores × 4′ 6″ stroke, and at 58½ rpm was offering 113 horsepower to machinery requiring 60.

This manufactory had 825 looms and the boiler plant was consuming 29 tons of coal per week. But if the indicator diagram figures given in the Classification are correct, then all was not well, particularly in the high pressure cylinder where the power generated was well below that in the low pressure one; respective ihps being 96 and 143 with corresponding average working pressures of 13 and 7 psi.

This may have been an engine of some years' service in need of an overhaul, probably requiring a new piston in the high pressure cylinder, and perhaps Manchester's original engine and the first horizontal one in Preston, but alas there is no evidence to date to support or refute such a possibility. What is known is that India and Manchester Mills were to have the first circular mill chimneys in Preston.

Towards the end of 1865, Joseph Clayton & Sons' Soho Mill in Fylde Road, then known as Dawson's Old Mill, was destroyed by fire with the loss of 25,354 spindles. Standing on the north

The Famine Years and a New Engine

33. A plan of India Mill in 1897.

side of Fylde Road and immediately east of the main West Coast railway line, the factory had been built sometime between 1832 and 1836 next to the canal bank. In 1842 Hugh and Arthur Dawson employed seventeen spinners there, working hand mules.

At the time of the fire, Clayton had recently acquired the mill from the Dawsons who had a new factory directly opposite in

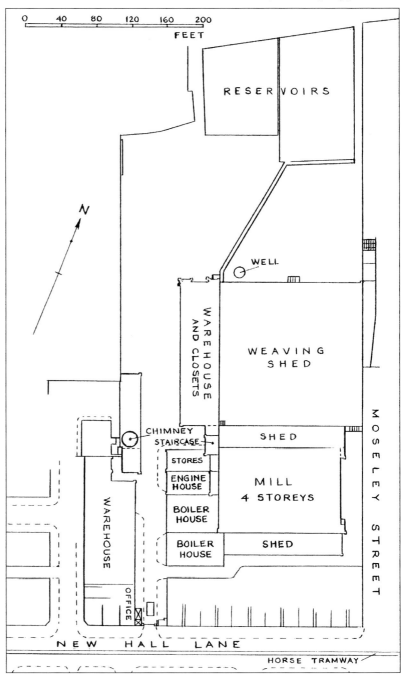

Fylde Road. The precise date when this factory was erected remains uncertain but a sound estimate is the early 1860s. Although the mill and its reservoir are shown on a large scale map surveyed in the 1840s and printed later from a transfer to zinc in 1882, this is a gross error on the part of the map maker. This example of the unfortunate practice of adding buildings and features to old maps at a later date without indicating these changes is mentioned later in connection with another Preston mill.

However, in the March list of 1862, there is mention of the 'Old side' and the 'New side' for Hugh and Arthur Dawson's mills, indicating that both Fylde Road mills were operating then, although under notice to close due to the Famine. In the new mill which had 568 looms, all stopped, 28,200 spindles on hand mules were at work six days per week, whilst in the old mill where 140 looms lay idle, 25,394 spindles on self-actors were in operation.

For the Trade Directory of 1865, Hugh Dawson is listed for the new Fylde Road Mill, but by 1869 the factory had taken on new proprietors, S. & J. F. Leese. William Dawson's Mill in Aqueduct Street was closed and that seems to have been the end of the Dawson family name in the Preston list. The Fylde Road factory was to stay under the control of the Leese family for years afterwards, but in 1896 Hartley Bros were the owners when a pair of McNaughted beam engines were driving 12,342 spindles for twist and 29,680 for weft. One engine had 31″ and 35″ bores on respective strokes of 3′ and 6′, whilst the second engine had 33″ and 38″ bores on respective strokes of 3′ and 6′; the combination running at 31 rpm. Three boilers for 60 psi pressure had been made by Clayton in 1866, and dates for the machinery were 1865, 1871 and 1882. The reason why the engine bore sets were not identical was possibly because one engine had been added later or had been rebored, probably in 1866 at the time of the new boilers; both engines then undergoing the McNaughting treatment years later, most probably in 1882.

On Saturday 13 June 1981 part of Fylde Road Mill was destroyed by fire, but fortunately I had visited the mill on 4 November 1977 to undertake an examination of its internal construction. At the time, many years had passed since its closure as a cotton factory.

The spinning side had been catered for in two multi-storey blocks, separated by the engine house which ran from the second floor to the top floor of the higher block of six storeys, the one nearest to Fylde Road. The first two floors of this block were 'fireproofed' by cast-iron columns, brick arches, iron beams and

The Famine Years and a New Engine

flag floors. This would have been the preparatory section with its highly charged atmosphere of cotton dust, vulnerable to the fire hazard. The remaining floors reverted to the usual 'non-fireproof' construction, that is, cast-iron columns, wooden beams and flooring, the sixth floor having been removed due to the dangerous condition of the flooring.

As to the second block, this had a cellar with three floors above, the whole structure being 'non-fireproof'. In both blocks the side walls were load-bearing, and in this second block they were sinking and bulging due to sand under their foundations. In the cellar the iron columns were standing on huge stone blocks and thus had not been affected by subsidence, but the sinking of the side walls had brought about curvature of the whole structure.

In the weaving shed, cast-iron columns supported wooden beams and cast-iron roof channels, the latter leading to a main drainage channel along which rainwater had passed en route to the condenser reservoir. On the shed site was an old well and during demolition of nearby houses, further wells were found.

After the fire of 1865, J. Clayton & Sons' Soho Mill in Fylde Road must have remained derelict for some time. In 1869, still listed under the name of Joseph Clayton & Sons it was closed, but soon afterwards opened up as a manufactory. James Wade was a manufacturer in 1873 with a Fylde Road address, presumably at Clayton & Sons' old mill, and in the early eighties Wade had 226 looms and employed 80 hands. By the middle of the decade he was no longer in the Preston list, and in 1889, Edward Hayes had a weaving business at Fylde Road Shed which would be the manufactory previously operated by Wade.

In 1887, Foster of Preston supplied a boiler, 7′ diameter × 28′ in length to steam at 80 psi pressure, which must have arrived for a new horizontal compound engine operating in the 1890s with 12″ and 18″ bores × 3′ 6″ stroke to drive 318 ordinary looms and 13 dobbies. It may well have been of the side-by-side type, and at 60 rpm was offering 24 horsepower to the machinery. Fylde Road Shed continued under the name of Edward Hayes to well into the early 1900s, but in 1910 was represented by Burton & Frost Ltd who were still its representatives in 1917. By 1922, H. Eastwood & Co. Ltd are at the Fylde Road manufactory and still listed for it in 1927 before closure came shortly afterwards.

Architecturally, the most impressive manufactory of the 1860s, indeed of the nineteenth century in Preston, was Alexandra Mill in Skeffington Road, off Ribbleton Lane. Erected in 1866 in an Italian Renaissance style, the manufactory was in the 1869 Trade Directory and represented by the executor of George Wilding. In 1882, having operated under the Wilding Brothers for a number of years, Alexandra housed 927 looms, and in the 1890s was operating on a horizontal compound engine, presumably a cross compound, which had 20″ and 37″ bores × 4′ 6″ stroke. It had been made by Fosters of Preston who had supplied two boilers in 1892 for a steam pressure of 120 psi, coal consumption being 29 tons per week.

The local firm of Joseph Foster & Sons had been founded in 1860 by Joseph Foster, the first foundry being in St Paul's Square. The making of printing press machinery in a large works in Bow Lane would become a major activity of the firm, which in 1887 would take over the Soho Foundry of Joseph Clayton in Greenbank Street. Here, in 1890, 550 hands and staff were employed in iron and brass foundry work, and the erection of boilers, engines, and printing machinery.

Fosters made delightful shed engines, and a cross compound example of theirs once ran at the Jacquard Weaving Company's Sunnybank Mill, Kirkham. Installed for the Room & Power Company who built the shed in 1907, the 450 horsepower engine named 'Progress and Perseverance' would give nearly fifty years' service before being replaced by electric motor drive. The cylinders, fitted with Corliss valves, had bores of 17″ and 34″

34. The engine house at Fylde Road Mill acts as a fine break in that it separates a spinning block on the left with another block housing preparation department and spinning flooers above, seen on the right.

× 4′ 6″ stroke. The boiler, also made by Fosters, steamed at 175 psi pressure, and engine drive was by 16 ropes from an 18′ diameter flywheel.

The engine at Alexandra Mill, Preston, probably arrived with the two boilers in the early 1890s replacing an engine whose identity is unknown. In the nineties, the new engine was running at 59 rpm, developing 242 ihp in its high pressure cylinder and 179 ihp in its low pressure one. Respective average working pressures were 53 and 11 psi, and 91 horsepower was on offer to machinery requiring 110. With 100 horsepower being taken, the engine appears to have been on overload. The manufactory also had a small vertical engine running at 80 rpm, which would be attending some preparatory or finishing process or possibly providing drive for a mechanics' shop as well.

Alexandra Mill was still operating under the name of Wilding Bros in 1966, before being demolished a few years later in the 1970s.

Directly opposite Alexandra Mill was Lutwidge Mill, a spinning factory which had a large five-bay block four storeys high, with a water tower at the south western corner. Although the factory did not exist in the 1840s or 1850s, nevertheless it is shown on the large scale (60 inches to 1 mile) Ordnance Survey Map which had been surveyed in 1847, engraved in 1849, and published on 29 September 1849; an error of a map maker of some years later. Every few years the Ordnance Survey would publish revised sheets, new impressions taken from the amended original copper plates.

36. Preston-built cross compound engine by Joseph Clayton & Co., for the Stonebridge Mill, Longridge. The Preston engine building firm also provided the two boilers.

37. 'Progress' and 'Perseverance, the cross compound engine supplied by J. Foster & Sons, Preston, for Sunnybank Mill, Kirkham.

Unfortunately, the engraver would not indicate this on the new plates so that each revised sheet would bear a date earlier than the one for the new publication, even though it had new buildings on it. Evidence of this practice can be seen in connection with the Lutwidge factory which was not in the trade directories of the 1850s nor the directory for 1860; and the first indication of the mill being in production is in the 1865 Trade Directory for Birley, Beaumont & Co.

An interesting feature of the Lutwidge Mill site was that it was never used to the full; at least half of the land area would remain vacant. One possible explanation could be that when the mill was being erected in the first half of the 1860s, it might have been the intention to form a combined establishment, but the effects of the Famine put an end to this plan, leaving spare land where manufacturing processes would have operated.

The mill was to be sold by auction on 16 March 1896, and in the notice for the intending sale it says, 'There is sufficient Land for considerable extension or for the erection of a New Mill or Weaving Shed'. At that time the Mill was freehold, free from ground rent, and had recently undergone some modernisation by way of new carding engines, roving frames, mules etc., as well as acquiring a water tower for a recently installed automatic sprinkler system by Dowson & Taylor. The capacity of the tower's tank was 5,000 gallons, and on each staircase, water from the town's main was available for fire fighting.

As well as the mill block, there was a two-storey warehouse, a one-storey carding shed, an engine house, boiler house, mechanics' shop, and a two-storey building housing cotton mixing and scutching rooms. Two reservoirs were also mentioned in the sale particulars, including an overhead refrigerator for condensing purposes, which would be an early type of cooling tower by which the engine condensate, after being pumped to the top of the structure, would descend through a series of wooden slats for its cooling. Such a device could at one time be seen on the Bold Street Mill site, the tower standing alongside Eldon Street.

In 1897, Lutwidge Mill had a compound horizontal engine which had been made by Rothwell & Co. Fitted with McNaught & Varley's patent cut off motion, the engine had 21″ and 39¼″ bores × 4′ 6″ stroke; average working pressures being 34 and 14 psi respectively to develop corresponding ihps of 164 and 236 at 50 rpm. One steel Lancashire boiler 8′ 6″ in diameter and 30′ in length, made by W. & J. Yates in 1890, was providing steam at 110 psi pressure, and had a set of Green's Patent Fuel Economisers with 96 pipes, made in 1893. There was also a steam pump for the sprinkler system, and a boiler by Dowson, Taylor & Co., the latter presumably being the 8′ high vertical boiler listed. Weekly coal consumption at the mill was 31 tons, and spinning for weft on 27,000 spindles was in operation for Messrs Birley, Beaumont & Co.

Some years previously, the main engine had undergone modification, which was noted in Yates's book of engines for 1876–84, Blackburn. The entry for 'Messrs Birley & Beaumont, Lutwidge Mills, Preston, Dec., 1879' was for a low pressure cylinder to be rebored and fitted with a new Ramsbottom Piston. This would be for the Rothwell-built horizontal compound as the engine speed listed was 50 rpm, tallying with the 1897 Classification figure.

Rothwell of Bolton was building horizontal engines in the 1860s, having supplied one to Low Moor Mill, Clitheroe, in that decade. The degree of work done on the Lutwidge engine at the end of the 1870s points to it having been in service for some years. Therefore one might conclude by suggesting that the engine, if not a second-hand one, was fitted in Lutwidge in the first half of the 1860s, and quite possibly was one of the first horizontal main drive engines in Preston.

Moor Park Mill in St George's Road is not shown on the Guardian Map of 1865 nor on the 1844–47 Ordnance Survey Map, yet it is listed for Gardener, Crankshaw & Co. in 1841 who were employing seventeen spinners in 1842. The mill is also mentioned in 1860 when it was the manufactory for Joseph Gillow who in 1862 had all of his 81 looms lying idle because of the Famine. Gillow is listed in 1855 as a manufacturer of muslin in St George's Road and presumably was the same entrepreneur who had been operating hand looms in Chapel Walk in 1841. Gillow's name is not in the 1865 Trade Directory list, so one assumes he was a victim of the Cotton Famine, and in 1869 Hall & Todd are manufacturing at Moor Park Mill. In 1873, John Todd & Co. are its representatives, listed as manufacturing linen as well as cotton in 1877. By 1880, Moor Park Mill had taken on Company Limited status, listed as Moor Park Cotton Manufacturing Co. Ltd, and in 1882–83 had 489 looms and employed 224 hands.

In 1896, the manufactory had 600 looms, its engine being a horizontal compound having 18″ and 32½″ bores × 5′ stroke. An indicator diagram taken in April showed that 86 ihp was being developed in the high pressure cylinder and 89 ihp in the low pressure one; a fairly well-balanced engine. Two boilers by Stevenson were in situ, with only one in use at any one time for 60 psi pressure, coal consumption being 18 tons per week. Unfortunately there was no information to indicate directly when the engine arrived as a replacement engine. However, Moor Park

Mill continued in the Preston list until at least 1927 before closure came soon afterwards following which it became the premises of F. Bamber, corn miller.

Why the mill was not shown on the maps mentioned remains a mystery when the square form of its chimney listed in the 1890s Classification indicates a pre-mid-1860s date of construction, in keeping with the 1841 reference or even a little earlier. Already mentioned in this chapter is that the first wave of circular mill chimneys in Preston began with the building of India and Manchester Mills in the first half of the sixties.

The decision to erect circular chimneys instead of the traditional square and octagonal forms was partly a question of economics in that the circular type required fewer bricks for the same height, hence a cheaper proposition. Also the aerodynamic aspect, albeit at a simple level, would mean its streamlined section would cope better with very high winds. However, it would be its streamlined section that in time would expose a major weakness of the circular chimney. In very high wind conditions, all industrial chimneys have a tendency to move backwards and forwards but more so the circular form. Such a phenomenon would be responsible for the cracking of mortar joints and brickwork on many circular chimneys which led to their multi-banding by metal clamps.

At the top of every mill chimney was the overhang, technically referred to as the oversailer, a projection of stone blocks held together by iron clamps, the purpose of which was to protect the brickwork from the sulphur-laden plume of smoke as it left the chimney in certain wind conditions.

Wind blowing against the stalk of a chimney would form an area of reduced air pressure down the leeward side to create a suction effect. Without an oversailer in position, this suction would tend to draw the plume down the side of the chimney, depositing soot onto the stonework or brickwork. The action of rain would soon convert this deposit into an acidic layer with its resulting destructive effect. Naturally, the oversailer itself and the metal clamps which held it together were subjected to this corrosion. Towards the end of the steam mill era, many oversailers were in a dangerous condition, and their removal became an urgent necessity. At Brookhouse Mills, the large circular brick chimney erected in 1872 had an oversailer made up of cast-iron segments held together by bolts.

Byelaws to control smoke pollution from industrial chimneys as much as possible were introduced, and every boilerman always kept a watchful eye on his chimney plume in fear it might encourage a visit from an inspector.

Of the three forms, the octagonal chimney was perhaps the

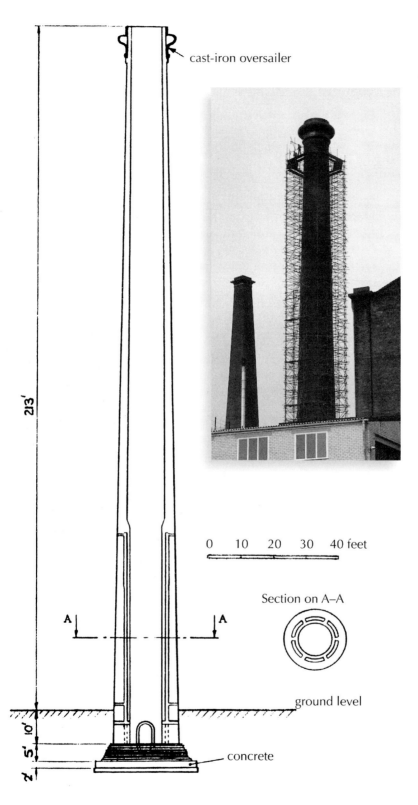

cast-iron oversailer

213'

A | | A

Section on A–A

0   10   20   30   40 feet

ground level

10'

5'

2'

concrete

38. Sectional elevation of the 1872 chimney at Brookhouse Mill.
39 (*inset*): a photograph during the demolition of the chimney in 1979.

most graceful in appearance, a good example being the one at Broomfield Mill which presented a series of ecclesiastical arches at its base. The one at Paul Catterall's New Hall Lane Mill in Maitland Street was another fine example before it was demolished in the 1970s. But whatever its form, every mill chimney had its protective lightning conductor and also access at its base for the periodic removal of soot.

Good draught to the boiler plant was essential, and for this reason the girth and height of a mill chimney was dictated by the size of its steam raising plant. The single or twin boiler plant of a manufactory would only require a chimney of small proportions compared to a three, four or even more, boiler installation attending a spinning or combined mill which would have a much larger chimney. Such a contrast in size could at one time be observed in comparing the chimney of Tulketh Spinning Mill with that of its near neighbour, Embroidery Mill, a manufactory.

Therefore at one time, a study of a town's mill chimneys in relation to their style and size could reveal if the town had had a long association with its textile industry, and if weaving had been more predominant than spinning or vice versa. In Nelson for example, the small circular chimney became dominant, illustrating that the main development of its mills came after the 1850s with specialisation in weaving. The final phase of circular chimneys in Preston arrived from 1904 onwards with the building of Cliff and Tulketh Mills and a number of manufactories, the final one thought to have been the 60-yarder erected at Peel Mill in *c*. 1920 and demolished in 1964.

The following is the Preston list of chimneys recorded in the 1890s Classification. The mills are arranged in alphabetical order and beginning with the square chimneys. Figures in brackets relate to their height in yards.

A List of Preston Square Chimneys (1890s)

ALBERT (35) base side 11';
ALLIANCE (44) base side 13';
ARKWRIGHT (51);
ASTLEY FIELD (25) base side 7';
AQUEDUCT (50) base side 14';
BOLD STREET (40);
BROOKFIELD (25);
BROOKHOUSE (40 yards above roof);
BUSHELL STREET (55);
CALEDONIAN (37) base side 10';
CROFT STREET (38) base side 12';
DEEPDALE (30);
FISHWICK (63) base side 20';
FRENCHWOOD (47);
FYLDE ROAD (44) base side 13' 6";
FYLDE ROAD SHED (25) base side 10';
HARTFORD;
HIGHER WALTON (90);

HOPWOOD STREET (12–13)
base side 6' 6";
HUNT STREET (60) base side
7';
GREENBANK (80) base side 20';
GRIMSHAW STREET (25) base
side 7' 9";
KAY STREET (28);
KENT STREET (40) base side
13';
LUTWIDGE (42) base side 12'
6";
MOOR HALL base side 14';
MOOR PARK (38);
MOSS SHED (40) base side 11';
NEW HALL LANE (25) base
side 10';
NEW PRESTON (63) base side
18' 6";
OXHEYS (35) base side 11';

PARKER STREET (50);
PARK LANE (50);
PRIMROSE (30) base side 10';
QUEEN'S (50) base side 12';
RIBBLETON (40);
SHELLEY ROAD (52) base side
16' 6";
SOUTHGATE (42);
SOVEREIGN (35);
SPRINGFIELD (40) base side 12';
STEAM (30) base side 10';
STOURTON (52) base side 14';
ST PAUL'S ROAD (36);
VICTORIA in Peel Hall Street
(42);
WELLINGTON (50) base side
15';
YARD WORKS – two, (45)
base side 13', and (54).

A List of Preston Octagonal Chimneys (1890s)

BANK TOP;
BROOMFIELD (40);
LORD STREET (43);

NEW HALL LANE in Rigby
Street (44);
PEEL (40);
POLE STREET (40).

A List of Preston Circular Chimneys (1890s)

ALEXANDRA (42) base dia. 13'
9";
ASHTON SHED (26) base dia.
9';
BROOKHOUSE (70) base dia.
22';
CENTENARY (63) base dia. 18'
on a square plinth;

FLATS (60) base dia. 18' 3";
INDIA (52) base dia. 13';
MANCHESTER (50) on a plinth
15' × 15';
MOORBROOK (45) base dia.
14';
SPA (60);
TENNYSON ROAD (45).

CHAPTER SIX

Ordeal by Fire – the 1870s

T HE DECADE of the 1870s is often referred to when the Great
Depression (1873–96) began, which many historians have re-
garded as a myth. Nevertheless, the Lancashire textile industry
did undergo considerable economic change during this decade,
beginning on a high note and ending on a low one. The years
1870 and 1871 were to represent one of the most prosperous
periods in Lancashire textiles, when there was an abnormal demand for textile goods from the Continent caused by the
withdrawal there of French and German operatives and artisans
from industrial employment due to the Franco-Prussian War. In
1872, the French and German manufacturing industries began to
recover and the demand for Lancashire textiles fell, although there
was still a demand for them in India and China.

This demand would encourage the mill-building boom of
1873–75 in Oldham where 72 limited spinning companies were
formed in three years. These limited companies raised capital
locally through the issue of shares and also the acceptance of
loans which gave interest. Thus the new mills became savings
banks. During this period, a mill-building boom was also evident
in Bombay, and by the late 1870s a reduction in the cotton trade
with India and China had come about.

In Preston, the economic progress of its textile industry
throughout the seventies would be low-key. No new spinning
mills would be erected in these years or those of the next decade,
and in contrast to the Oldham industry, the Preston one was the
bastion of private enterprise. In essence, Preston had not fully
recovered from the blight of the Cotton Famine, and the
mill-building programmes of the fifties and early sixties were not
to be a feature of the seventies. On the contrary, many Preston
firms, small and privately owned, were to carry on their textile
businesses in old buildings with ageing machinery and engines of
some years. Other textile firms, large family concerns supported
by their standing reputation, were to enjoy some degree of
prosperity during these years of business instability, but even in
this particular sector, new building activities and extensions were
severely limited because of the economic climate. In the weaving

trade, only one major new manufactory would be added to the Preston lists, this being the mill for the Tennyson Road Cotton Spinning & Manufacturing Co. Ltd.

Mill fires, as in the sixties in Preston, would be a regular feature of the seventies, destroying thousands of spindles in the spinning sector. The old Preston spinning mill blocks, many of which had been built years before on the 'non-fireproof' principle, with wooden floors tinder-dry and impregnated with tallow and oil, were highly inflammable, and with gas lighting were most vulnerable to the ravages of fire. How many mill buildings were insured is questionable. The buildings and stock destroyed in a fire of June 1847 at Wellfield Mill, for example, had not been insured.

Steam Mill on the northern side of Fylde Road, and alongside the main West Coast railway line was a cotton manufactory under new ownership in 1870.

The site upon which it stood had formerly supported a flax spinning mill and a corn mill, and it was from the latter that the manufactory had taken its name. This connection of name came to light in a notice for an auction that was to take place on 21

40. A plan of Steam Mill in the 1890s.

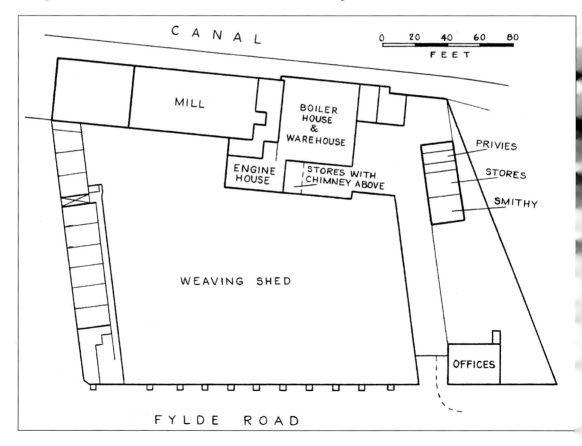

41. The impressive terracotta work showing the splendid monogram of Joseph Eccles' initials and date on the office block facing Fylde Road at Steam Mill.

September 1812, at the corn mill, then named Steam Mill. In the auction would be the corn mill's steam engine of 16 horsepower, boiler, flywheel weighing 3 tons, bevel wheels and upright shaft, spur wheel, stones and milling machinery etc. All this machinery had been new six years previously and had been in working order four months before. Instructions were such that a rent would be required if the materials were worked or remained on the premises, and for further particulars, enquiries were to be made to Roger Hind, Millwright, Preston.

The 1844–47 map shows the flax mill and the corn mill adjacent to one another, with the Lancaster Canal at the rear and a large open frontage area to Fylde Road. This frontage space had been built upon by the time the town map of 1865 was published, and in 1862 there had been a reference to Steam Mill when John Swainson had 350 looms there. Swainson also had 480 looms at this time in Leighton Street Mill, which had been shown on the 1846–47 map as a flax spinning mill. The flax connection with Swainson was in the Trade Directory for 1865, when, under cotton manufacturers, his name was listed for linen as well. For the Preston Trade Directory lists of 1869 there is no mention of Steam Mill, but by 1870, the mill had passed into the new ownership of Joseph Eccles & Company, cotton manufacturers.

The present-day remains of the mill bear evidence of the new company in the splendid monogram of Joseph Eccles's initials complete with the date of 1870, all in terracotta on the front of the office block in Fylde Road. The office building itself is executed in the bright red machine brick of the late nineteenth century or early twentieth century period, and thereby was erected years after the formation of the company.

In the 1890s Classification, the engine for Steam Mill was described as: 'compound horizontal, 1879, altered', the date presumably being when it was made. Cylinder bores were 18″ and 32″ × 5′ stroke, and for 36 rpm, respective ihps were 119 and 98. Sixty three horsepower was on offer to the machinery.

The engine was situated near the centre of the site and obviously, because of its location, had been installed to drive a weaving shed on the frontage area, the mill having 600 looms in 1882 when 300 hands were under its employment. Near the engine house stood the chimney, its square sectional form being a reminder of the time when the site housed the flax mill whose multi-storey block would be used as a preparation block when the conversion came about for cotton weaving.

A Sale Directory of November 1920 for the Steam Mill of Messrs Joseph Eccles & Company lists the various uses the floors of the old flax mill block had been put to.

It was described as the main brick mill, 6 storeys high, 73′ 3″ by 38′ 3″, the floors listed as:

1st storey.	Weft warehouse 10′ 0″ high
2nd storey.	Twist warehouse 9′ 6″ high
3rd storey.	Winding and warping room 9′ 6″ high
4th storey.	Winding and warping room 9′ 6″ high
5th storey.	Looming room, heald and reed store 10′ 0″ high
6th storey.	Tape sizing and mixing av. 16′ 0″ high

The first floor, that is the ground floor, was flagged as was part of the second floor, the rest being boarded on wood joists, and there was a brick arched ceiling over part of the ground floor with cast-iron beams. The inventory drawn up by a Manchester firm of auctioneers and valuers also mentioned three Lancashire boilers. The boiler house and engine house were built in stone, and for years after the inventory had been drawn up, Steam Mill continued as a manufactory, listed for Joseph Eccles & Co. Ltd in the 1936 Trade Directory before it was closed.

Richard Threlfall's Broomfield Mill of 1835, just off the bottom of North Road, was burnt down in 1871 with damages amounting to £30,000. Neither Threlfall's name nor that of his mill appear in the Trade Directories of 1873, 1874, 1877 or 1880, so it would seem that the site remained derelict for some years. In the mid-1880s John Anderton, who also owned Grimshaw Street Mill, was manufacturing cotton at Broomfield Mill where in the 1890s a single compound tandem engine was offering 95 horsepower to the machinery. Cylinder bores were 22″ and 34″ × 5′ stroke, and at 50 rpm, 196 ihp was being generated in the high pressure cylinder and 99 ihp in the low pressure one.

It is most likely that this engine was installed when Anderton took over at Broomfield, replacing a beam engine which, had it not been damaged by the fire of 1871, would undoubtedly have been in a very poor condition after lying idle for so many years.

In the 1869 Trade Directory, Broomfield had been a combined concern but its change of status after the fire, to manufacturing only with a horizontal engine, was to be a common trend in the Preston industry during this period.

At about 4 o'clock in the afternoon of 28 May 1872, Grimshaw Street Mill was burnt to a complete wreck with the loss of 18,000 spindles. The mill had been erected around 1835 and was opened the following year when it appeared on the town map, and in 1869 was a combined factory for John Walker.

The mill engine must have survived the inferno because in the 1890s a single cylinder beam engine of 36″ bore was at work, coupled to a single cylinder horizontal pusher of 20″ bore. The combined engines, operating on 6′ strokes and running at 24 rpm, were driving 723 looms to be reduced to 565 as the 20-year-old boilers were condemned by the insurance company. The boiler pressure of 65 psi was also to be reduced to 60 psi. Indicated horsepower generated in the beam engine was 85, whilst for the pusher engine a figure of 120 was achieved. Horsepower available to the machinery was 97; 52 was required but only 50 was being used.

After the fire, the mill is absent in the Trade Directories for 1873 and 1874, but in 1877 it is the manufactory for John Anderton. An entry for that year in Yates of Blackburn's book of engine lists for 1876–84 mentions a high pressure engine for Anderton of Preston, which would be the pusher installed in Grimshaw Street Mill; the 20″ bore, 6′ ⅝″ stroke, and speed of 24½ rpm recorded more or less tallies with the data written for the 1890s Classification. The Blackburn firm's records also mention the cylinder being fitted on an old frame, and the 3¹⁷⁄₃₂″ diameter piston rod is referred to as the 'old rod'. This may refer to a second-hand engine being fitted with some alteration, or more likely, an engine that had been in situ for some time undergoing repair and modification.

Two boilers for 80 psi pressure were made in 1873 for Moss Shed which was in Fylde Road, almost opposite St Peter's Church, to attend a horizontal compound engine which arrived the following year. In the 1890s it was driving 585 looms, its cylinder bores being 14″ and 23″ × 4′ stroke. An engine test in October 1896 showed that 80 ihp was being generated in the high pressure cylinder and 107 in the low pressure one at 66 rpm. Only 36 horsepower was available to the machinery, and coal consumption of the steam generating plant amounted to 30 tons per week.

Moss Shed, alongside which ran Kirkham Street West, was on the old Moss Factory site which had been established by John Horrocks in 1797. Two spinning blocks stood on the site in 1832 for Horrockses, Miller & Co.; one was a new structure housing 10,496 spindles, whilst the older building accommodated 5,576 spindles. The factory was under the same ownership in 1874, but in 1880, William Smith & Co., who also had Queen's Mill, were manufacturing at the Moss Factory. In 1889, the manufactory is listed as Moss Shed for Walsh & Cocker who were weaving at Ashton Shed as well in the same year. Walsh & Cocker were still representing Moss Shed in 1892, but in the Trade Directory of 1898, only S. P. Cocker is listed, who continued for some years afterwards. The manufactory is listed in 1910 as Moss Shed (Preston) Ltd, remaining under this title for Guild Year, 1922, but it closed in the same decade.

In 1951, Moss Shed was a slipper manufacturing works for J. Berry & Sons Ltd. The old engine house with its external staircase complete with iron balustrade was then a storeroom, at the end of which ran the long narrow alley which had been used for transmitting the engine drive into the weaving shed. The original mill block, end-on to Fylde Road, and still standing at the time of writing, was a dance hall and furniture storeroom. At one time there had been a donkey engine on the site which operated on a 6″ cylinder bore × 9″ stroke, and drew water from the nearby canal.

On 2 July 1874 fire destroyed ten pairs of hand mules and as many pairs of self-actors, in all 27,500 spindles, at John Goodair's Brookfield Mill at the corner of Fairclough Street and Brookfield Street. The mill had been erected at the beginning of the 1840s and before its demolition in 1986 a date stone could be seen with a curious omission. It read '184 ', the fourth figure being obliterated, and thereby hangs a tale. It tells of a stonemason about to start work on the figure 'o' being approached by one of the owners, Napier (the other partner apparently being Goodair) who asked him what he was doing. 'Nowt', replied the stonemason, who was sacked on the spot, hence the omission.

Eventually the factory came under the sole ownership of the Goodair family, J. and T. Goodair having 34,408 spindles and 519 looms there in 1862 as well as 44,504 spindles and 896 looms at Peel Mill. Before the sixties ended, John Goodair & Company were to have Brunswick Mill under their business banner as well as Brookfield & Peel. All three mills were still under the Goodair name in 1892, but shortly afterwards Brunswick closed. Peel was taken over by a newcomer to the Preston scene, J. R. & A. Smith Ltd, whilst Brookfield would come under the control of John Liver who had made a move from Kent Street Mill to Brookfield sometime between 1892 and 1894, at the same time retaining his manufacturing business at Victoria Mill in Peel Hall Street.

In 1894, Yates & Thom of Blackburn made a horizontal cross compound for Brookfield, the engine driving 950 dobbies in 1896 when a new weaving shed had recently been built at the eastern end of the site. Cylinder bores were 15″ and 28″ × 3′ 6″ stroke. One set of corresponding average pressures was listed as 44.3 and 12.05 psi, whilst a second set was recorded as 51.3 and 12.35 psi. For 73 rpm, indicator diagram results were showing 131 ihp in the high pressure cylinder and 117 ihp in the low pressure cylinder. Two boilers were in situ with only one in use offering a steam pressure of 96 psi.

During the summer of 1978, I had the opportunity of meeting the ex-engineer of Brookfield Mill, the late Arthur Taylor who was seventy nine years of age at the time. He clarified that the cylinder bore diameters of the Blackburn-built engine of 1894, which had been under his care, were the same as listed in 1896, but gave the stroke as 4′ 6″ and rpm at 72. He also told me the names on the engine which were those of John Liver's daughters: 'May' for the high pressure engine, and 'Adela' for the low pressure one. Both boilers had been made by the same engine firm, Yates & Thom, and in Mr Taylor's time at Brookfield they steamed at 100 psi pressure, the engine running on a 25″ vacuum to produce 400 horsepower. Corliss valves were fitted on the high pressure cylinder and slide valves on the low pressure one. The flywheel, about 25 feet in diameter, was grooved for 7 ropes of 2″ in diameter which drove the first motion shaft of 15″ in diameter from which the drive was transmitted to 34 shafts, 20 of which were for the weaving shed. About 1,000 looms were in operation along with their preparation machinery.

Mr Taylor also gave an interesting account of the daily routine in the engine room and boiler house at Brookfield. The engine tenter (not to be confused with the engineer), who was also the boilerman, would arrive at 6 a.m. to stoke up for raising the steam pressure, which would take about 30 minutes. Lubrication and warming-up of the engine were his next tasks, ready for the arrival of the engineer at 7.15 a.m. for a 7.30 start, the engine running until noon then again from 1 p.m. until 5.30.

Saturday mornings would be spent by the engineer carrying out any necessary engine repairs which could be undertaken by him, and on Sunday mornings he would attend to his duties until noon during which time the engine would have been run for a half hour to rid the cylinders of water that had accumulated due to condensation during the stoppage period. Water left in cylinders could have disastrous consequences as engine staff at Leigh Spinners Mill, Leigh, for example, were to realise when they were left with a wrecked engine.

As was usual for a mill engine, the one at Brookfield performed better in winter when the condenser feed was colder than in summer, thus enabling a greater vacuum to be attained. If loading was taken rapidly off the engine – for example, machinery being suddenly shut down – the engine governor would fail to respond, immediately causing the engine to overrun.

Such a phenomenon was common on all engines in such circumstances, and at Tulketh Mill in Balcarres Road, on the final working day before the Christmas break, this phenomenon presenting itself on the large horizontal cross compound there could be spectacular. As the Christmas celebrations began in the mill, there could be a sudden stoppage of machinery without prior warning to the engine room. The huge engine would suddenly be

42. A plan of Brookfield Mill in the 1890s.

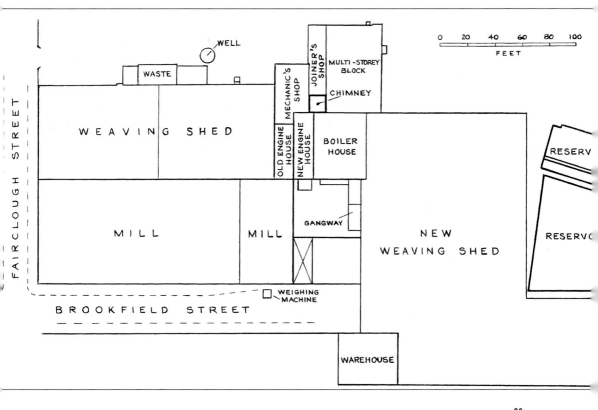

43. Demolition of Brookfield Mill (built in 1840) in 1986. The short, square-sectioned chimney was a typical example of its period. In the background is Moor Park Mill, pictured here many years after having undergone its conversion to a corn mill.

seen struggling violently with the unexpected drop in loading, much to the annoyance of the engineer.

The Brookfield Mill engine of 1894 was installed in a new engine house adjacent to the old one, the chapel-style end window of the latter still facing St George's Road for years afterwards until demolition of the site was undertaken in the 1980s to make way for a DIY store.

To the east of Brookfield Mill was Brunswick Place Mill at the bottom of Brunswick Place (later re-named Rye Street), off Kent Street. This small factory was occupied by Francis Lambert & Co. in 1825, Lambert having been spinning master at the Lord's Mill in Dale Street. In 1828, Lambert, Stephenson & Co. are the representatives, and in 1841 George Cooper & Sons are in control. A decade later Thomas John Garrington is spinning at Brunswick Place Mill and still there in 1857, but in 1860 the mill is absent from the Trade Directory. In 1865, it is operational again, spinning for Thomas Goodair & Co., and in 1869 John Goodair & Co. were its representatives, the factory continuing under this name until at least 1892 before closure soon afterwards. In consequence of this, Brunswick Place Mill would not be listed in the mid-1890s Classification, and unfortunately no engine data has been found for the mill which after closure accommodated a cabinet-making business for many years.

Considering its relative short association with the Preston cotton industry, its life as a spinning factory was not without serious

Ordeal by Fire — the 1870s

44. The old engine house (seen in the centre of the photograph) at Brookfield Mill, standing alongside a weaving shed with its characteristic saw-tooth roof incorporating north-facing windows.

45. Cast-iron columns and wooden beam construction in a weaving shed at Brookfield Mill.

incidents. A fire in 1866, mainly confined to the western end of the mill, was responsible for damage amounting to £4,000. But the mill's darkest day was 31 August 1848, when a boiler explosion caused the loss of seven lives.

This tragedy came only weeks after another boiler explosion at Sovereign Mill, Stanley Street on 17 June, when seven lives were also lost.

In 1830, cotton mill engines were operating on steam pressures at only 6 or 7 psi, a figure which had doubled a decade later and one which continued to increase rapidly as more powerful engines became available. During the 1830s and early 1840s, steam was still being generated as it had been in the 1820s, in boilers of the Waggon and single flue cornish type or any number of variants with a cylindrical form having flat or hemispherical ends. All were of crude construction and soon found to be most unsuitable in meeting the increased pressures demanded by the new engines.

Although the problem was solved to some extent by the introduction of the twin flue Lancashire boiler, patented in 1844, boiler explosions would still occur with frightening regularity as working pressures soared still further. In the Lancashire boiler the large undivided volume of water and the severe rocking strains in its structure whilst in operation made even this boiler susceptible to explosion if due care was not taken.

By 1850, boiler explosions had reached the dimensions of a

national scandal, yet it was not until 1882 that the first Boiler Explosions Act reached the statute book. In 1854, the Association for the Prevention of Steam Boiler Explosions, later known as the Manchester Steam Users' Association, was founded, followed by a similar society in Huddersfield. These two associations merely inspected members' boilers and took engine indicator diagrams, but the practice of taking out insurance connected to the system of periodic boiler inspection came with the formation in 1858–59 of the Steam Boiler Assurance Company, which ultimately became the Vulcan Boiler & General Insurance Company.

As the Lancashire soon became the standard boiler in the textile industry, many safety features were incorporated within its basic design. On top at the front was the dead weight value which blew when the stipulated working pressure was exceeded by 5 psi. Further along the boiler was the combined safety valve for high steam and low water, the former working by a dead weight and the latter operating on the principle of buoyancy, using balance weight, lever and float. Next came the steam supply valve followed by the manhole which gave access into the boiler for periodic de-scaling and inspection.

A reliable and necessary safeguard against damage or explosion in a Lancashire boiler arising from a shortage of water was the fusible plug made of gunmetal. Varying in size from 1″ in diameter to just over 2″, it was screwed into the furnace crown from the water side of the furnace tube. A removable cone containing an inner cone, held in position by a fusible metal, was then screwed into the plug from the water side, one end of the fusible metal being subject to the heat of the water, whilst the other end was acted upon by the hot gases. In the event of a shortage of water and the removable cone becoming uncovered, the fusible metal, without the cooling effect of the water, melted. This caused the inner cone to fall into the furnace, leaving a hole in the tube through which steam came to put out the fire. A regular check on water level was met by water gauges on the front of the boiler, above which was the steam pressure gauge.

Entry to the flues for cleaning was by two doors at the front end, and at the rear end of each side flue was a damper plate for regulating the draught. These plates could be lowered or raised by a system of ropes, pulleys and balance weights, the latter sometimes positioned in front of the boiler or behind it on the upper floor of the boiler house.

The practice of producing superheated steam had become common by the 1890s, achieved in the Lancashire boiler by passing the 'wet' steam through tubes situated immediately at the rear end of the boiler in the path of the flue gases.

46. A plan of Bank Top Mills in the 1890s.

Ordeal by Fire — the 1870s

On 3 December 1873 at Park Lane Mill in North Road, fire was responsible for £10,000 worth of damage, and on 12 August 1875, it struck again to cause a loss of £30,000 when 23 pairs of mules were destroyed. The factory had been opened in 1832 for Paul Catterall, Sons & Co., who employed 19 spinners there in that year, the firm moving to new premises in Rigby Street in the 1850s.

Park Lane Mill was a large combined establishment with a

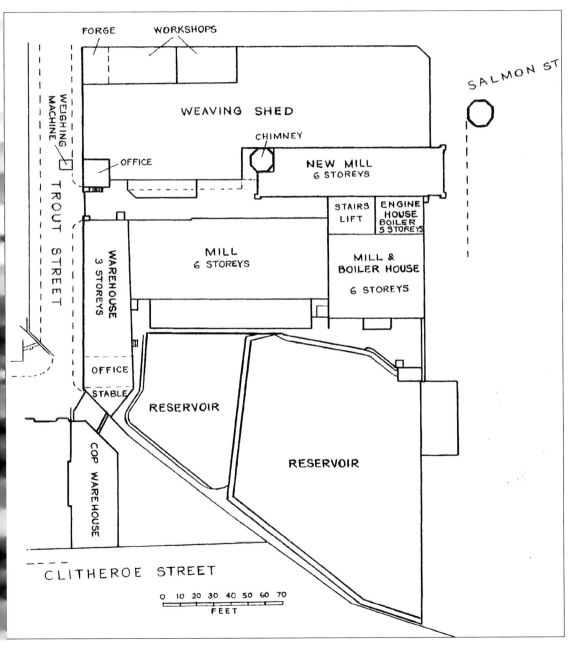

87

spinning block alongside John Street North and weaving facilities in Sedgewick Street. In 1862, it was under the control of J. A. & T. Simpson, who had 36,432 spindles and 830 looms there, and after the fire of 1875 the spinning block was rebuilt on the 'fireproof' principle and designed to accommodate mules having nearly 1,000 spindles each.

For the new factory a horizontal compound engine would provide the drive, replacing what had been a beam engine, probably a pair of engines of single cylinder or McNaughted form, recorded in 1897 as:

> The engine was put down when the mill was rebuilt after fire and in place of oscillating engines.

The large bore dimensions of the horizontal engine at 30″ and 50″ × 6′ stroke are a good indication that it must have been of the cross compound type, and the respective ihps of 201 and 203 point to a well-balanced engine. Boiler pressure was 80 psi, and spindleage was made up of 12,288 for twist and 37,696 for weft. Power available for the machinery was 199 horsepower of which only 100 was being used; the reason for such a large surplus of power was explained in the Classification of 1897.

Apparently it had been the intention to drive two sheds and the mill on the new engine. However, in the 1890s, the mill side was operating under the Park Lane Twist Company, and in the Park Mill Shed alongside Sedgewick Street were J. R. & A. Smith, who in 1895 owned Peel and Manchester Mills as well. The Park Mill Shed in 1897 still had its old engine, a McNaughted beam engine offering 114 horsepower to its machinery and running on a boiler made by Clayton in 1875. There was also a second boiler, an old one used for heating in winter. The other shed on the site was empty, so in 1897 the Park Lane Mill cross compound engine, much relieved of the labour it had been intended for, was considered twice the size needed for its work.

The rebuild of the Park Lane Mill, or Park Mill as it was often referred to, presented a most impressive spinning block four storeys high, sixteen bays long and four bays wide. Segmental brick arches running at right angles to the main iron beams rested on cast-iron filler beams spaced at about 38″ centres within the main iron beams of the 'fireproof' structure.

The development of the 'fireproof' factory has a long and interesting history, the first multi-storey building of this type being a six-storey cotton mill designed by William Strutt and erected in Derby in 1792–93. Two rows of cast-iron columns supported heavy timber beams which carried brick arches, the spandrel space above the arches being filled with sand onto which were laid brick tiles. The exposed underside of the beams was protected from fire by about 1½″ of plaster, with sheet metal covering the wooden skewbacks from which the arches sprang.

In 1796, Charles Bage, whilst erecting a flax mill in Shrewsbury using some of Strutt's techniques, would take the 'fireproofing' a stage further by using iron beams in place of timber ones. However, others did not immediately copy Bage's new technique, because of previous instances of cast-iron beam failure. For a compressive stress loading situation — for example, supporting columns — cast iron was reasonably safe, but subjected to tensile stresses as in beams, its use could end in disaster.

Early on in the nineteenth century, wrought iron was recognised as an extremely valuable material to use where tensile loading was involved. Yet it would not be until after mid-century that large rolled sections of the material could be produced as structural members. Difficulties arose in the manufacture of wrought-iron beams of considerable length because a 'puddling' furnace could only provide a small 'bloom' of the metal at any one time. A bloom was the iron in its semi-molten state taken from the furnace whence it was rolled and beaten, or 'wrought', to achieve the grain characteristics which could cope with tensile loading. Prefabricated wrought-iron plate box girder beams, the plates riveted together, appeared in mills after 1845 to allow arches of wider span, thus offering greater floor space between supporting columns. However, in general for cotton mills, wrought iron was used for tie rods in conjunction with cast-iron beams and brick arches.

One of the earliest examples of a complete fireproof mill in Preston was erected probably in the 1820s at Horrocks' Yard Works. The seven-storey block certainly existed in 1836 along with another seven-storey block, fireproofed throughout, named Field Mill whose engine house bore a date stone of that year. Field Mill was fourteen bays long and three wide. Years later it was fitted with a water tower executed in the red brick of the turn of the century period, its elaborate corbelling and colour contrasting markedly with the somewhat austere style and colour of the earlier building's fabric.

Water towers containing header tanks to provide the necessary water pressure for fire hydrants had begun to appear before mid-century on Preston's mills, the first phase of tanks being simply perched upon the towers, exposed to the elements as at Brookhouse, Arkwright and Hartford Mills. By the 1860s, new water tower construction saw tanks being enclosed within the towers as at Shelley Road Mill and in the 1880s rebuild at Aqueduct Street Mill. The sprinkler system, invented in America in 1881 and used in conjunction with the water tower, was a welcome development in fire fighting.

December 1875 saw fire damage amounting to £25,000 at William Paley's new Bank Top Mill in Salmon Street, off London Road. The factory had suffered fire damage costing £10,000 in January 1873, and after the inferno of 1875 there was another in April 1880, causing £6,000 worth of damage.

The building of Bank Top Mill had begun in 1823, the factory being listed for cambric manufacture and cotton spinning in 1825 for Richard Riley who was at Bank Top in 1855. William Paley was spinning at the mill in 1862 as well as at Stanley Street Mill, and in 1865 both mills were still under his control when they were listed under Cotton Spinners and Manufacturers in the Trade Directory. Bank Top Mill had 28,568 spindles and 230 looms in 1882, and was still operating under the Paley name when it closed as a combined establishment in the 1920s only to reopen as a manufactory, which was operating under the name of John Clarke Ltd, in 1926. Years later in 1966, the same firm still represented the Bank Top manufactory.

A visit in January 1992 to the site found surviving buildings almost unrecognisable as once being part of a cotton mill. At the southern end, the lodge area had long since been filled in. To the north, three bays of a four-bay boiler house had been bricked up, the other bay having a doorway to an automobile repair shop. Close by remained an engine house of narrow proportions, which in 1896 had housed a horizontal triple expansion tandem engine. The 1890s Classification lists its makers as Mason & Goodfellow of Blackburn, but this may be an error in that the makers were more likely to be Clayton & Goodfellow of Blackburn.

The engine had originally been installed as a single tandem compound engine, the third cylinder arriving later to be the new high pressure one in the final triple tandem arrangement. This was a common practice for raising the power of an engine where space was limited. The bores of the three in-line cylinders, that is, high, intermediate, and low pressure, each sharing the same piston rod, were 16″, 24″ and 45″, respective average working pressures being 73, 19 and 6 psi. On a stroke of 3′ and for an engine speed of 64 rpm, corresponding ihps were 169, 82 and 115, and horsepower available to the machinery amounted to 82.5. The engine in its two-cylinder form probably arrived after one of the three major fires mentioned to replace a beam engine, its conversion to triple expansion working possibly taking place in 1894 when Fosters made a boiler for 156 psi pressure. In the 1890s, a small vertical engine with a 6″ bore × 9″ stroke was providing drive for the mechanics' shop, whilst for the sizing department a horizontal engine of 6″ bore × 9″ stroke was in attendance.

On 25 November 1876 fire gutted the top three storeys of a four-storey spinning block at Moor Brook Mill in Moor Brook Street, the bottom or first storey being of 'fireproof' construction. The erection of the six-storey block had been under way in 1852 when it was demolished by a gale on Christmas Day. In consideration of the loss on the contractors, the mill owner accepted a four-storey block instead.

This building activity of 1852 had been part of a major reconstruction of the site to take on weaving, the original spinning mill having been completed in the 1830s for a Mr Crankshaw. Even the reservoirs were re-sited from the northern to the eastern end, and as well as the new four-storey block, two weaving sheds were built, a twelve-bay one at the western side and a smaller shed at the south eastern corner. Near the entrance in Moor Brook Street was a two-storey block, part of which was for winding, whilst on the southern end of the spinning block would be a beam engine house and boiler room. Following the fire of 1876, the four-storey block was rebuilt, and whilst there are indications that spinning machinery was installed, spinning operations would only be short-term as the Moor Brook site eventually became manufacturing only.

Crankshaw had been in partnership with a Mr Smith in 1842, but the 1851 Trade Directory lists only George Smith as a cotton spinner at Moor Brook, and in 1855 he was manufacturing in the new sheds. In 1862, Smith and his son had 23 pairs of hand mules and 400 looms idle due to the Famine, and the factory was closed in 1869. In 1873, Moor Brook Mill was operating under Joseph Smith who was also the proprietor of Southgate Mill nearby. At the same time Farnworth & Livesey were listed under manufacturers for Moor Brook old mill, Moor Lane. By 1877 Moor Brook Mill in Moor Brook Street had taken on John Livesey as a manufacturer; retained Joseph Smith as a spinner and manufacturer; and was listed under Cotton Spinners and Manufacturers in the Directory as Moor Brook Mills Co. Ltd. When the 1880 directory was published, Smith had left Moor Brook which still went under company limited status but by 1882, spinning had ended at the mill, Thomas Livesey manufacturing there with 644 looms. In 1889 two separate firms were weaving at Moor Brook, John Anderton and J. R. & A. Smith Ltd, and in 1895 the Moor Brook Mill Co. Ltd is listed under cotton manufacturers.

The engine plant recorded in the 1890s for the mill represented a pair of McNaughted beam engines which would have been laid down in the early 1850s as a pair of single cylinder engines for the new combined mill layout, to be compounded later, probably just prior to or immediately after the fire of 1876.

During the nineties, in their McNaughted form the engines were driving 760 looms, each having identical high pressure cylinder bores of 29¾″ × 3′ stroke and 33″ low pressure cylinder bores × 6′ stroke. Average corresponding working pressures in one engine amounted to 20 and 5.3 psi to give respective ihps of 72 and 48.9 at 30 rpm. Figures for the other engine were 22 and 5.8 psi for 80 and 53.5 ihp respectively. Steam pressure from the two boilers was 55 psi which accounted for a coal consumption of 4.9 lbs per hour per ihp which amounted to 32 tons weekly. The two engines were offering 240 horsepower to machinery which only required 70 horsepower and were obviously coping well with what would have been a much-reduced system of transmission which followed the abandonment of spinning years earlier. The factory's circular chimney, probably an addition of the seventies, stood on the southern side of Moor Brook Street.

One of the problems recognised early on in multi-storey non-fireproof factory construction was the tendency for the main wooden floor beams to be crushed by the weight exerted upon them by the cast-iron columns on the floors above. To overcome this, and also to present a more stable construction, cast-iron box-like objects with two opposite open sides, termed 'saddles', were fitted to the top of the columns through which the wooden beams passed, thus allowing the crushing weight to be taken via the saddle to the column below.

During the 1970s, I was able to photograph the saddles in the old multi-storey block.

Moor Brook Mill continued in the manufacture of cotton goods until at least 1936, closing shortly afterwards, and eventually the buildings were occupied by Crompton & Barnes, wholesale joinery undertakers. My 1970s visit found the old mill block windowless to provide cross-ventilation for timber seasoning and storage, its top storey having been removed. On the valley floor the first storey, which would have been used for the cotton carding process, was 'fireproof' with cast-iron beams and brick arches. At the southern end was the engine house, its large end window opening having been bricked up; and in the ceiling there were still the eyebolts, used in hoisting up the huge beam bobs of the engine into position by rope and tackle. Demolition of all the buildings was undertaken in the 1990s to make way for the present DIY superstore.

J. Eccles & Co.'s Ashton Mill was destroyed by fire in January 1879, along with 22 pairs of mules amounting to 32,000 spindles.

Situated in Bridge Road, this spinning mill was absent from the 1844–47 Ordnance Survey map but was listed in 1857 for Anderson, Irving & Company. Anderson & Crompton are there in 1860, but in 1869 William Crompton is the sole proprietor, still spinning at the mill in 1874. In 1877, the mill is under the control of the Eccles brothers, but after the fire of 1879 it remains absent from the Preston lists for some time before appearing as Ashton Shed, a manufactory for Richard Walsh & Company in the Trade Directory of 1885–86.

Claytons had made a boiler for the mill in 1878, followed by another in 1883 when the horizontal engine listed in the 1890s was probably installed to run the new manufactory. One assumes that the circular chimney was erected around this time as part of the rebuilding programme. The horizontal engine listed in the 1890s Classification was a single cylinder version with an 18″ bore × 5′ stroke, and at 45 rpm was indicating a nominal horsepower of 43. The full 36 horsepower on offer to the machinery which required 34 was being taken, and with a boiler pressure of 80 psi, six tons of coal were consumed daily, and loomage amounted to 471 looms.

Ashton Shed was to have a long association with the Preston industry; the manufactory was represented by Turnbull & Yates Ltd in the Guild Years of 1922 and 1952, as well as in the Trade Directory of 1966.

A new manufactory opened in the second half of the 1870s in the eastern suburbs of Preston was the Tennyson Road Cotton Spinners & Manufacturing Co. Ltd Mill, listed under Cotton Manufacturers for 1877. The building of Tennyson Road Mill came at a time when there was a growing confidence in horizontal engines as prime movers in Lancashire textiles. The heyday of the traditional type beam engine was over, and although the next decade would see the compounding of a number of Preston beam engines in pursuit of higher powers, such procedures were common sense economics, as the alternative would be a costly changeover to one of the new type engines which were becoming available in either horizontal or vertical form.

The engine driving 475 looms (including 180 dobbies) at Tennyson Road in 1897 was a horizontal single compound tandem of 14⅛″ and 24⅛″ bores × 5′ stroke. Respective average steam pressures were 37 and 13 psi to give corresponding ihps of 105 and 110 at 59½ rpm. A horsepower of 41.8 was available to machinery of which 40 horsepower was being taken to satisfy a requirement of 39. Fosters had made a boiler during the previous year for 100 psi pressure, weekly coal consumption to be 20 tons in summer and 26 in winter, and whilst the tandem engine could have arrived with the new boiler, it may well have been the original engine. However, the drive from engine to first motion shaft was belt, an innovation at this time in power transmission. In 1906, an engine house was built next to the tandem engine room, and in March 1912, there is mention of a bill of quantities for proposed alteration and additions to the mill for Samuel Slater, who was representing the manufactory in 1917, and with his son in the 1920s. Tennyson Road Mill would change to a 'combined' status for John Barnes & Sons Ltd, its representatives under Cotton Spinners and Manufacturers in 1932 and years later in 1966.

Quite a number of mill limited companies were formed in the 1870s in Preston, one being the Preston Cotton Spinning & Manufacturing Co. Ltd established in 1874 at Wellfield Road Mill, a factory which had started in c. 1834. In 1851, it was the combined mill of William Bashall junior, who had 32,380 spindles and 800 looms there in 1862. The new limited company at Wellfield Mill would be of long standing, from 1874 until at least 1926, but in 1932 the mill came under Lancashire Cotton Corporation Ltd, closure coming soon afterwards, following which the site was taken over by the English Electric Co. Ltd. In the early 1900s, Wellfield Mills received two horizontal cross compounds, one a 1905 Musgrave engine with 18″ and 38″ bores × 4′ stroke for number two mill, to produce 550–600 horsepower at 68 rpm, working on 160psi pressure. The second engine, a Yates & Thom example of 1908, with 25″ and 52″ bores × 5′ stroke, drove number one mill, producing 1,200 horsepower at 64rpm whilst working on a 145–160 psi pressure.

The Oxhey Cotton Spinning & Manufacturing Co. Ltd, Oxheys Mill, was in the Trade Directory for 1877. Three years earlier it had been listed under Cotton Spinners and Manufacturers for E. T. Gardner, Oxheys Mill, Brook Street. The factory, not to be mistaken for Oxheys Mill in Aqueduct Street, is included on the 1844–47 Ordnance Survey Map and shown relatively isolated in the old Preston Moor area, which at the time was undergoing building development as mentioned earlier. In 1851, the mill was represented by Gardner & Naylor who are listed in an Assessment of 1844. Oxheys Mill was still operating under limited company status in 1917 but it would leave the Preston lists soon afterwards, its multi-storey block remaining until 20 December 1948, when it was destroyed in an serious fire one evening.

A beam engine is listed for the mill in the 1890s which had 20″ and 38″ bores, each cylinder generating 209 ihp at 44½ rpm; corresponding average working steam pressures being 50 and 13 psi. It was an engine seemingly being worked to its limit in that even though it was offering 96 horsepower, 98 horsepower was being taken to drive machinery requiring 104 horsepower. Engine revolutions were a little on the high side for a beam engine, and whilst the figure quoted for the high pressure cylinder stroke is not at all clear in the 1890s Classification because of the fine pen script of the period, it could read 5′. If this is correct and being therefore the same dimension as the stroke of the low pressure cylinder, we have here an indication of what could be a horizontal engine. Further support for the possibility of a horizontal engine is the large difference in the bore diameters, and also an examination of the layout of the mill which shows the engine house area divided into two sections labelled 'engines'. So with some caution, I am suggesting the distinct possibility that a pusher engine of the cross compound or side by side type was installed at some date in an adjoining engine room to an ageing beam engine: and that at the time of the 1890s valuation the latter had been scrapped or disconnected, leaving the pusher engine to cope on its own, leading to its apparent overload. If this is true, then the listing of 'Beam' for the engine at Oxheys Mill in the 1890s Classification is incorrect.

However, at the time of the valuation, the two boilers by Stevensons at the mill were eleven years old, placing their date of manufacture at around 1885–86. If the engine running at the

47. A plan of Oxheys Mill in the 1890s.

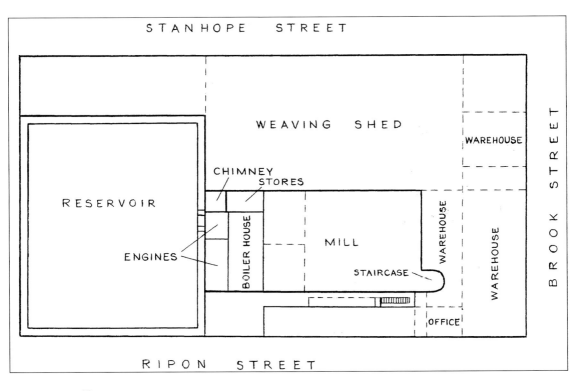

mill was indeed a horizontal one, then its installation most probably coincided with the arrival of the boilers. What is clear is that the mill was in a poor state during the nineties. It had no hoist, a poor floor, and a shed roof in bad condition, with operatives having to carry throughout a distance of 100 yards from the scutching room.

Amongst the last of the mill fires creating havoc during the seventies in Preston was the one in February 1879, at Horrocks & Jackson's New Mill in Avenham Street which was burnt down containing twenty pairs of mules amounting to 30,000 spindles; damages were put at £30,000.

The huge six-storey block, nine bays long and six broad, and known also as 'The Big Mill', had been added in 1850 to a long-established factory listed in the Trade Directory of 1816 as a spinning concern. By 1818, it housed a combined spinning and manufacturing business for Horrocks & Jackson, its address being Turk's Head Court, where John Horrocks had begun his cotton empire. In 1851, it is referred to as Turk's Head Mill for Horrocks, Jackson & Co., and eventually Avenham Street Mills, under the same ownership. The firm survived the fire of 1879, having 53,000 spindles and 70 looms to employ 200 hands in 1882–83, but shortly afterwards it went into closure, its absence noted in the Trade Directory of 1885–86.

CHAPTER SEVEN

Modernisation Schemes of the 1880s

T HE 1880s began on an optimistic note for Lancashire textiles, the industry experiencing a boom between 1881 and 1884. In Preston, this economic upturn coincided with the Guild Year celebrations of 1882 to bring about a much-welcomed initiative for enterprise, expansion, and modernisation in the factories.

By now, having achieved its conquest over the beam engine as the recognised prime mover behind spindle and shuttle alike, the horizontal engine was gaining much popularity. It was now possible to work these new type engines on steam pressures of about 80 psi to achieve good economic working, using Corliss valve gear which had been patented by the American, G. H. Corliss, in 1849 and first imported into Britain in 1859.

Early horizontal engines were fitted with the well-proven slide valve, but as working pressures rose it became obsolete, the superior Corliss valve gear allowing closer governing to be achieved thus giving a much smoother drive, essential to avoid thread breakages in spinning. It was common practice to fit Corliss inlet valves at the top of a cylinder, and outlet valves at the bottom, an arrangement which ensured that the inlet valves were never cooled by the exhaust steam from the outlet valves, thus making for high steam economy. Contrary to this practice, J. & E. Wood of Bolton positioned both sets of inlet and exhaust Corliss valves at the bottom of their engine cylinders with apparent success.

However, it was the introduction of rope drive from America to Lancashire mills at the end of the 1870s that would finally unleash the full working potential of the horizontal engine. The old drive system, in which cast-iron spur wheels with bevelled gear wheels turned upright shafts from which the drive was transmitted to various floors in multi-storey mills, was heavy and thus power-absorbing. These extremely noisy geared drive systems, many operational in Lancashire factories until well into the twentieth century, necessitated expensive and very precise installation procedures to ensure the correct alignment of drive components. Also, the failure of a cog in a gear wheel could result in a costly and lengthy repair involving a long shutdown.

Rope drive, quieter, faster and more even than geared drive, would present a new architectural dimension to the cotton factory; the projecting engine house. The drive arrangement involved a number of ropes passing around the grooved flywheel of the engine, to run to a number of grooved drive pulleys positioned in a rope race and aligned to the various drive shafts of the mill floors.

Much thought had to be given to the positioning of these pulleys; a rule to be observed whenever possible was that no pulley's centre line should be higher than 45 degrees above an imaginary horizontal line drawn through the centre of the engine's flywheel. This rule allowed the upper side of a rope, which was the idle side, to sag in a free curve so making a larger contact with its pulley, adding more power to the drive shafting. To establish this 45 degree angle, the engine and its flywheel had to be positioned an appropriate distance away from the drive race, hence the projecting engine house.

In the situation where rope drive was to replace a geared drive arrangement, the rule had to be ignored in many instances due to the lack of projection space and the need to use existing drive shaft centres on the mill floors. In such circumstances, an interesting 'back driving' system could result involving the zig-zagging of ropes from pulley to pulley as at Paul Catterall's New Hall Lane Mill in Rigby Street. At some mills, annexed glass-sided drive races were constructed on the ends of the old mill blocks to accommodate the ropes from new engines, a practice seen at one time at Yard Works.

With rope drive, large flywheels, many in excess of 24′ in

48. Section through the engine room and rope chamber at the Howe Bridge Spinning Co.'s No. 3 Mill. The diameter of the rope drum (flywheel of the engine) was 34 feet and had 34 grooves. It weighed an astonishing 85 tons and rotated at 47 rpm.

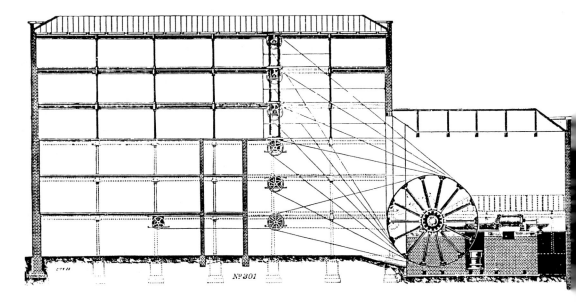

diameter, became common to produce peripheral velocities exceeding 5,000′ per minute. Another advantage of rope drive over geared and belt transmission was that if a rope broke, the mill was able to continue working because of multi-rope pulleys being adopted. In a large rope race it was usual to have under each set of ropes a thin rod holding in a stop button connected via a battery-run electric circuit to a 'stop motion' mechanism on the starting valve of the engine. On breaking, a rope would dislodge the rod to release the stop button and so bring the engine to a standstill.

It was not uncommon to have flywheels accommodating 40 or more ropes, the vee grooves being at an angle of 40 or 45 degrees to prevent the ropes from reaching the bottom of the grooves thus eliminating wedging. Special care was taken to ensure that each rope fitted exactly at the same depth in the grooves as the rest, so ruling out the possibility of some ropes taking on more load than others which would result in uneven driving and unnecessary wear on them.

Ropes were made of cotton which gave them strength, flexibility, elasticity, and resistance to excessive stretching, although by the end of a working week some sagging could be observed. After a rest over the weekend the ropes would have tightened again. Humidifiers were often employed in rope races to produce an atmosphere that would help to maintain the properties of the ropes, and with careful usage a rope could have an average life of at least twelve years.

One of the first mills in Preston to adopt rope drive was Wellington at the corner of Fletcher Road and Deepdale Mill Street. Erected in the first half of the 1850s it was the factory of the Wellington Mill Spinning Company in 1855 and by 1857 it had taken on loomage to become the combined establishment of Goodair & Napier. In 1862 the partnership had apparently ended with Goodair operating at the nearby Peel Mill and Brookfield, leaving Napier with his own company at Wellington where he had 31,140 spindles and 380 looms. George W. Napier & Company were at Wellington in 1874 but in 1877 H. C. Outram & Company of Manchester and Castle Street Mills had taken over at Wellington. Outram was still at Wellington in 1880, the year in which Clayton & Goodfellow of Blackburn made a horizontal compound engine for the mill, which judging from the bore sizes was possibly of the cross compound type. One cylinder or engine was named 'Gladstone', the other 'Bright'. During 1896, with 24″ and 43″ bores × 5′ stroke it was running at 51 rpm to provide rope drive to the spinning rooms; respective average working pressures were 31 and 11.1 psi.

A single McNaughted beam engine was also running, providing wheel drive to preparatory machinery including carding. Its bores were 28½″ and 35″ on respective strokes of 3′ and 6′, engine revolutions being 33 rpm. Four boilers were steaming at 80 psi, two having been made in 1876, most likely for the compounding of the beam engine. The other two boilers had been made in 1882 by Claytons; the disparity between this date and that for the horizontal engine could well be an indication that the engine did not commence work until Guild Year due to the installation of rope drive. Spindleage in 1896 at Wellington amounted to 34,448 spindles of which 18,128 were for twist and the rest for weft. There were 618 looms.

Clayton & Goodfellow had begun engine building in 1860 and were renowned for their fine horizontal cross compound engines. One of their engines made in 1867 ran in a Blackburn mill until 1972. In 1876 the engine firm produced a horizontal compound engine for Lostock Hall Spinning Co. Ltd. Three boilers had been made by Stevensons in the same year and in 1898 were steaming at 86 psi with a coal consumption of 50 tons per week. Engine bores were 28⁹⁄₁₆″ and 52½″; corresponding average working pressures were 30 and 10 psi.

Probably the last surviving Clayton & Goodfellow engine was the horizontal cross compound built in 1914 for a Chorley weaving shed. Looms from Northrop in Blackburn had failed to arrive because of a strike, and as war was breaking out, Leyland Motors moved in for the production of motor lorries for the war effort. The engine was to run a generator by rope drive, the generator being No. 28608 of the Lancashire Dynamo & Motor Co. Ltd at Trafford Park in 1915. Two visits to the Chorley Works, one in 1975, the second ten years later, found the engine, generator, and switchboard in excellent condition considering they had lain idle for some years, but in 1988 the engine was dismantled and placed into storage. The last mill engine to be built by Clayton, Goodfellow & Co. Ltd was a uniflow one in 1922 for Bee Mill, Ribchester.

Wellington Mill was not alone in adopting the new rope drive in the early eighties in Preston, as William Calvert & Sons were also to adopt the new technology in the same period.

On a visit to the archives of the North Western Museum of Science and Industry at its old site in Manchester in 1979, I found a drawing made by Musgraves of Bolton entitled 'Details of Patent Starting Gear for Messrs Calvert & Sons', dated 1 May 1882. The drawing showed a flywheel grooved for rope drive, its periphery having 312 cogs at 3¹⁄₁₆″ pitch for the engagement of the starting gear. This gear, or barring engine as it was commonly

49. Mills in the North Road area, looking northwards. Centre are Park Lane sheds next to the spinning block of Park Lane Mill, with reservoirs behind. Immediately northwards is Bute Mill, then Kent Street Mill, while west of Bute Mill is Hanover Street foundry with Hanover Mill (then a slipper works) at its northern end. On the centre right of the picture is Astley Field Mill.

known on mill engines, was fitted to the flywheel of large engines for starting them from cold or for moving them slowly in the event of repairs or maintenance. On starting an engine, the barring engine, which was a steam engine unit itself, drove the flywheel until it had gained sufficient speed for the main engine to continue on its own, at which point the barring engine automatically became disengaged.

In 1882, Musgraves of Bolton built a horizontal single tandem compound engine for Flats Mill number two at Walton-le-Dale, belonging to William Calvert & Sons, and there is no doubt that the starting gear shown on the drawing of 1882 found in Manchester was for this engine. Figures recorded in the nineties Classification show the engine as having 31″ and 52″ bores × 6′ stroke; respective average working pressures were 32.4 and 11.5 psi to generate 400 ihp in each cylinder at 45rpm.

By the early 1870s, William Calvert & Sons of Walton-le-Dale, with Flats and India Mills under their ownership, had taken on

Aqueduct Street Mill, the Trade Directory of 1873 confirming this.

Aqueduct Street Mill, often referred to as Oxheys (not to be confused with the mill of that name in Brook Street) was a spinning factory in 1842, having recently been erected, but by 1851, with the addition of looms, it was the 'combined' mill of Hugh and William Dawson. It was the scene of a fire on 21 August 1868, and was closed the following year before being bought by Calverts in 1871. Brown's Map of Preston of 1883 shows its 1840s layout but a map of 1889 presents a different plan of the factory, indicating that a rebuild had recently taken place, a date of 1887 for new boilers bringing the time of the rebuild into sharper focus.

For the new factory complex, two multi-storey blocks faced directly onto Aqueduct Street, behind which was a large weaving shed on the valley bottom and a three-storey block on its western side for warping and winding. Also to the west was the new reservoir, overlooked by the large square chimney of the earlier mill, and under the weaving shed and in direct east-west alignment with the reservoir was the culverted Moor Brook.

The westernmost six-storey spinning block, ten bays long and five wide, had been raised on the non-fireproof principle with wooden beams of yellow pine on cast-iron columns fitted with saddles, the whole structure complete with cellar. The second six-storey block, unlike the other which rose directly adjacent to

50. The two blocks, with water tower between them, arising from a rebuild of the 1880s, of Aqueduct Mill, sometimes referred to as Aqueduct Street Mill. In the distance is Brookhouse Mill, its chimney in scaffolding in readiness for demolition.

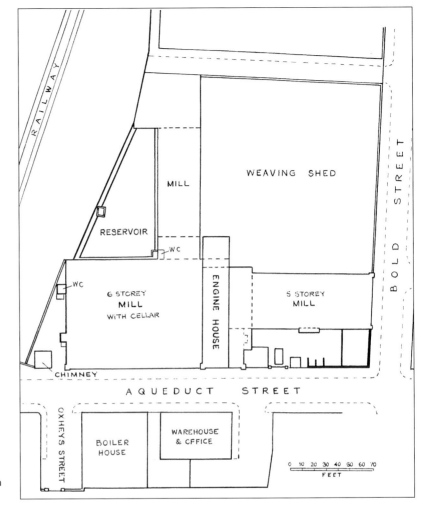

51. A plan of Aqueduct Mill in the 1890s.

the street pavement, was set some distance back to offer an unloading area for the baled cotton, as this was to be where the preparatory processes would take place. Only two bays wide and with a single row of supporting pillars, the first three floors would be tiled with a supporting structure of 'fireproof' brick arches and iron beams; and in both mill blocks their longitudinal walls were load-bearing.

In comparison to quite a number of Lancashire mills of a similar size erected during the eighties decade, the overall external features of Aqueduct Street Mill were plain, even somewhat austere. Its only feature of any architectural merit was its water tower executed in an Italianate style, which today still makes a notable contribution to the town's skyline in the wake of extensive site demolition which has taken place over the years.

Site area for the mill was at a premium when one notes that the five-bay boiler house was built on the opposite side of

104

Modernisation Schemes of the 1880s

Aqueduct Street to the engine room, the steam pipe passing under the street. Such a distance from boilers to engine would bring about a drop of 10 psi steam pressure in the engine room from a boiler pressure of 90 psi.

Three boilers, each 8′ in diameter and 30′ in length, had been made locally by Fosters in 1887, and in 1896 were attending a large single tandem compound engine which must have arrived for the new mill complex. Cylinder bores were 31″ and 52″ × 6′ stroke, and with respective average working pressures of 25½ and 11 psi, corresponding ihps of 315 and 382 were being developed at 45 rpm. At the time, the factory had 7,192 spindles for twist, 18,160 for weft, and accommodated 627 looms. Horsepower available to the machinery amounted to 214 of which 150 was being taken, the machinery requiring 132; and a coal consumption figure was recorded for the nineties Classification as 3.75 lbs per hour per ihp.

The engine room, situated between the two mill blocks just mentioned, was long and narrow in keeping with a tandem engine installation, and had a 'fireproof' brick arched ceiling clad in wood panelling. Rising to three storeys, its drive race would also act as a firebreak between blocks, and as the northern end of the engine room extended outwards from the mill blocks, this was a firm indication that rope drive did arrive for the rebuild.

On comparing the general dimensions and performance figures for each of the tandem engines at Flats and Aqueduct Street Mills respectively as listed in the 1890s Classification, it became clear that the engines must have been identical and were approaching the largest size permitted for this type of engine. Assuming that the engines had been installed as standard examples by the Bolton firm of John Musgrave & Sons, the driving drum on each engine must have been about 30′ in diameter and grooved for approximately 26 ropes. These figures relating to the driving drum were laid down in a standard list of single tandems by Musgraves about this period, and corresponded to an engine of 139 tons gross weight having 28″ and 52″ bores × 6′ stroke. Working on 100 psi pressure, the engine would generate 1,090 ihp at 50 rpm. Musgrave's largest standard engine of the single tandem type weighed 170 tons and had a driving drum 30′ in diameter, grooved for 28 ropes.

These final figures were impressive for any type of engine but for a single tandem were considered to be the ultimate, as the off-set position of the rotating drum with its immense centrifugal forces could place tremendous stresses on the engine's components. For higher powers, the more well-balanced layout of the cross compound engine or the perfect-balanced arrangement of the twin tandem compound engine (see Chapter 8) was

AQUEDUCT MILL PRESTON. WEAVING.

AQUEDUCT MILL PRESTON. WINDING.

106

Modernisation Schemes of the 1880s

54. Weaving shed, Aqueduct
Street Mill.
(*Harris Museum, Preston*)

55. Winding room, Aqueduct
Street Mill.
(*Harris Museum, Preston*)

recommended, but alas these two types did require wide engine rooms.

In 1885–86, Wellington Mill in Deepdale Mill Street was under the ownership of Eccles Bros who at this time were also operating at Victoria Mill in nearby Peel Hall Street, and New Hall Lane Mill, opposite New Preston Mills at the town end of New Hall Lane.

Victoria Mill had been raised in the early 1850s, the factory in 1855 being under the control of Henry Sharples & Company, cotton spinners and manufacturers, who were still there in 1880. In 1882 the mill, then under Eccles Brothers, had 18 pairs of mules amounting to 28,724 spindles, and in 1882–83, J. Liver & Company were also operating at Victoria, manufacturing with 475 looms and employing 220 hands.

In 1886, the two companies were still operating at Victoria, the year when Yates of Blackburn were to build an engine for the Preston factory which would provide rope drive from a 24′ diameter driving drum. The engine would be a vertical compound type, described in the 1890s Classification as 'two vertical cylinders working directly onto crank which is below them', this description indicating a single crank vertical compound. In such an engine, the high and low pressure cylinders were adjacent to one another to turn a single crank by means of a triangular connecting rod as illustrated in figure 64. This arrangement of the cylinders and connecting rod ensured that the engine could never be stopped in a dead-centre position which is why it was often referred to as a 'vertical non dead-centre engine'. Other types of engine, which unfortunately did stop in a dead-centre position, could only be re-started with the aid of the barring engine.

The idea behind the application of the triangular connecting rod appears to have originated with Galloway's patent of 1839 and revived by Bernays in the 1870s. Little progress was made until the 1880–1907 period when Fleming & Ferguson's and H. J. H. King's patents were developed.

Running at 56½ rpm, the Victoria Mill vertical which had 28″ and 51″ bores × 5′ stroke was working on respective average pressures of 31 and 7½ psi to achieve corresponding ihps of 322.5 and 261.8, according to an engine test taken in 1895. Three boilers made by Clayton in 1856 were steaming at 65 psi to use 80 tons of coal per week, and the engine's performance must have been retarded to a considerable degree due to this low steam pressure from a boiler bank which would have arrived for an earlier beam engine installation. Spindleage for the mill in 1896 amounted to 15,972 for twist and 12,752 for weft, and there were 572 looms.

An alternative arrangement for a single crank vertical compound engine was the cross compound version, where high and low pressure cylinders were fitted opposite one another, each having its own crank with the driving drum in between. But in whatever version the vertical engine appeared, the compactness of its layout, which was one of its virtues where engine room space was limited, could present difficulties in cleaning and maintenance in comparison to a horizontal engine.

Another Preston factory to operate under the name of Victoria was situated off Marsh Lane, near the Victoria Quays. Apparently it was the mill recorded by Tulket in 1821 as having been built in 1817 and known as Kaye's Mill, but it was yet another Preston factory never to make the 1890s Assessment. In 1851 it was the combined establishment for John Paley & Co. and six years later was the spinning mill for William Humber. Stott Brothers & Co. were there in 1873, S. H. Stott being the managing director of the spinning and weaving concern in 1880 before closure. By 1889, James Briggs, corn merchant, had his business established at the mill, still known as Victoria but listed as Marsh Lane Flour Mill in 1892, and Ribble Flour Mills in 1913. A photograph in John Mortimer's *Industrial Lancashire* (1897) shows the main multi-storey block with a water tank perched aloft an adjacent tower, converted into a flour mill with rooftop ventilators. At the south-east corner may be seen the free-standing square chimney, whilst to the west, near a smaller multi-storey block, is the reservoir wall.

Mill fires which had blighted the seventies in Preston were also to be a predominant part of the eighties scene. Maynard's Dale Street Mill was to be a victim in 1881, and in 1883 at William Nimmo's Tulketh Factory in Water Lane where 160 hands were employed, 32,720 spindles were destroyed.

Erected in 1835 as a spinning mill for William Taylor, Tulketh Factory was operating for the Fylde Road Spinning Company at the time of the fire, following which the buildings were eventually demolished; the 1912 Map shows the site vacant at the bottom of Tulketh Brow. Although the factory had been in close proximity to the canal, its site had supported a large reservoir.

Fire fighting equipment during the eighties was ineffective against such mill infernos, Preston having only three fire engines in 1883, two manual ones and a steam operated one; the latter had been purchased in 1872 from Messrs Shand, Mason & Company of London. One of the town's earliest schemes for the provision of water for fire fighting as well as for public consumption was begun in 1729, resulting in the collection of water into a cistern situated in what was to be the Glover Street area. Taps at certain points enabled the sale of water, and five water plugs were positioned for fire fighting.

Modernisation Schemes of the 1880s

The first engine of the Preston Fire Brigade was a manually operated one with two force pumps, the water being brought to the engine in buckets. New engines were delivered in 1827, and land and buildings were purchased in Woodcock's Court, but in 1831 more convenient premises were established in Avenham Street. A more powerful manual engine, 'Victoria', arrived in 1837 and another manual, horse-drawn engine named 'Prince of Wales' came during the 1840s. 'Prince of Wales' could project water to a height of around 85′, whilst 'Victoria' was reputed to be capable of reaching 15 yards higher than a six-storey warehouse. On 24 May 1852, the foundation stone was laid for a new fire station in Tithebarn Street, and in 1871 costs were laid for trials to decide whether to buy a Shand, Mason & Company steam-operated engine or a Merryweather & Son engine. It was agreed in the 1880s that horses for pulling the Shand, Mason & Co. engine would be provided by the Corporation. In April 1881, with the advent of the telephone system, a request was made for a free-of-charge wire from the telephone exchange in Lancaster Road to the fire station, permission being granted in December of that year. Motor traction came to the Preston Brigade in 1914.

Hewitson in his *History of Preston*, published in 1883, was to clarify the sorry state of the Preston cotton industry at the time by writing:

> For some time, the cotton trade at Preston has been in a dull retrograde state, neither the enterprise nor the activity manifested a quarter of a century ago is now apparent. There are no new mills put up in these days. Weaving sheds and kindred structures have increased in number. But it is about 20 years since an additional mill was erected in Preston. And it is, furthermore, a fact that very few of the mills which have been burned down during these years have been rebuilt. In quite recent times – within, say, the past ten years – some mills have been shut up or entirely pulled down, whilst others have been utilised for purposes in no way connected with the cotton trade.

By 1883 the drift of spinning to the south of Lancashire and a growing predominance of weaving in the north had become evident, yet Preston continued to enjoy to some extent the position it had earned as an important centre for both spinning and weaving, the Preston District accounting for 2,191,552 spindles and 48,243 looms in 1882–83. The three largest firms were Horrockses, Miller & Co. employing 3,000 hands; William Calvert & Sons with 2,218; and John Hawkins & Sons who had a workforce of 1,581.

During the eighties, Preston was ranked fourth largest in Lancashire in the list of spinning towns, with Oldham at the head, Bolton in second place, and the immediate area around Manchester taking third position. In weaving, Preston was the third largest of the manufacturing towns, Blackburn being in second place and Burnley in top position. Whilst Preston was to maintain its weaving ranking position for years afterwards, the town's standing in the spinning table list had dropped to fifth position by 1903; Rochdale had moved into third place at the expense of Stockport which was now in fourth position.

Following the spinning mill building boom of 1873–75 in Oldham, mentioned earlier, further expansion would take place in 1883–84 and 1889–90 to produce 19 more limited companies in Oldham, and between 1904 and 1908 another 28 would be listed. From having 240 mills in 1883, increased to 281 by 1906, by 1918 Oldham could account for 320. In contrast to the Oldham industry which favoured public-run mill limiteds to a large extent, the Bolton industry went mainly for the privately run limiteds, and like Preston was also a large preserve of the family-run firm.

In the weaving districts of north-east Lancashire during the booms of 1889–92 and 1893–94, the privately run limited company did achieve some degree of popularity, especially in the main centres of Blackburn, Burnley and Nelson, but least so in Preston. So the Preston industry, a citadel of private enterprise was to seal its own fate and would be a shadow of its former self when the 1930s dawned.

On 2 April 1885 John Humber's Bushell Street Mill off Lancaster Road, containing 32,912 spindles on mules and 12,700 on throstles, was burned down. The factory is not mentioned in the Trade Directory for 1841 nor in an Assessment for 1844, but is shown on Myers's Map of 1846, the first structures being a mill block which would be the one destroyed in 1885, a square chimney, and a large boiler house which in 1895 belonged to the Electric Light Company. Expansion for weaving facilities came soon after 1846, and in 1851 the factory is listed under Cotton Spinners and Manufacturers for the Humber Brothers. In 1857, John Humber was the proprietor and was still representing the factory in 1869, but on John's death, James Humber was the executor, his name appearing for Bushell Street Mill in 1873, and until at least 1880. By 1882–83 John Humber junior was in charge, employing 570 hands.

After the fire of 1885, the mill would be engaged in manufacturing only for John Humber; and soon after 1895 T. Brotherton & Company took over the manufactory where in 1897, a horizontal compound engine was running at 41 rpm with 20″ and 36¼″ bores × 6′ stroke.

A test in October 1896 had shown 108 ihp in the high pressure cylinder and 105 ihp in the low pressure one; a well balanced engine but one considered to be three times too big for its workload and thought to have been an old one purchased from some other mill. The engine must therefore have been in situ for some time, probably arriving with two boilers, one made by Stevenson and the other by Clayton, both of which were eleven years old in 1897, the year when the manufactory had 500 ordinary looms and 130 dobbies. Around 1900 or just afterwards, a three-storey preparation and warehouse block was erected to face North Road, complete with a handsome water tower which fortunately still graces the skyline.

When Brotherton & Company arrived at Bushell Street they were also manufacturing at Marsh Lane Mill in Hunt Street where they had been since at least 1882 when the manufactory had 560 looms. Brotherton had arrived at Marsh Lane Mill to succeed Gardner & Welsh who were in business there in 1880, having been representatives of the manufactory since at least 1855 when it was new to the Preston lists. In 1836 the site had supported a flax mill, and in 1846 presented a cotton and flax spinning factory known as Sherrington Mill. In 1896 Marsh lane Mill was known as Hunt Street Mill, its engine being a horizontal compound of 18″ and 32″ bores × 5′ stroke. Driving 196 ordinary looms and 380 dobbies, the engine was considered 'not fully weighted', its high pressure cylinder producing 126 ihp and its low pressure one offering 80 ihp. One boiler by Stevenson, 8′ diameter × 28′ in length was steaming at 80 psi; the engine offering 71 horsepower to machinery requiring 44 horsepower, although 55 horsepower was being taken.

During the 1880s, to the immediate north of Bushell Street Mill, and off Lancaster Road near St Thomas's Church, was a manufactory known as Lawson Mill. It is shown on Myers's Map of 1846 at the bottom of Ormside Street with a large reservoir to the west backing onto Moor Lane. Most likely a newly erected steam-powered establishment at this time, it had developed on a site laid out some time between 1836 and 1841 apparently for handloom cotton weaving, James Park having handlooms in Lawson Street in 1841.

Over the next three decades at least, quite a number of small and short-lived textile businesses were to operate in this area, some with a Lancaster Road address such as George Faulkner & Co., cotton manufacturer listed in 1851 and 1855; Fallows & Keymer manufacturing there in 1857; and James Lawson, the latter still weaving in this particular area in 1860 when another firm is listed, Hobday & Nichols, who were cotton spinners and manufacturers. In early 1862, Nichols is working all of his 112 looms, six days per

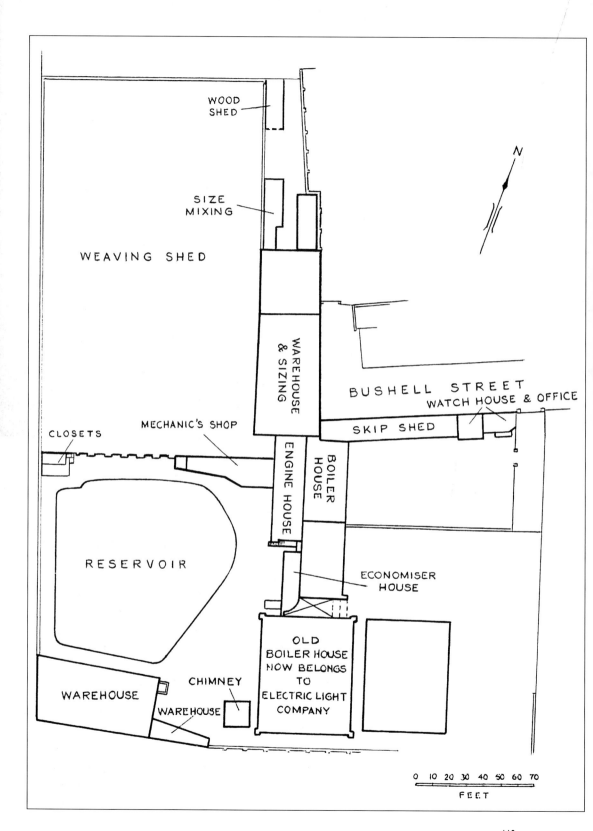

WOOD SHED

SIZE MIXING

WEAVING SHED

WAREHOUSE & SIZING

N

BUSHELL STREET

WATCH HOUSE & OFFICE

MECHANIC'S SHOP

CLOSETS

SKIP SHED

ENGINE HOUSE

BOILER HOUSE

RESERVOIR

ECONOMISER HOUSE

CHIMNEY

WAREHOUSE

WAREHOUSE

OLD BOILER HOUSE NOW BELONGS TO ELECTRIC LIGHT COMPANY

0 10 20 30 40 50 60 70

FEET

112

57. Bushell Street Mill, with its shed area flanked by a block used for warehousing and housing preparaion machinery, complete with water tower.

week, and George Brown is cotton spinning five days per week with three pairs of self-acting mules, with a Lancaster Road address. Nichols & Brown are still in business in 1865, when Robert Towers, who also sold cement and plaster of Paris, is weaving gingham in Lawson Street; and in 1869, Woods & Hampson are weaving at a Lancaster Road address and also manufacturing at Swillbrook Mill in James Street, off London Road.

Therefore it would seem that Lawson Mill did at one time accommodate several small business enterprises on a room and power system whereby space, machines and steam power would be available on rental, and such a system was probably introduced by William Shaw & Company who are listed for Lawson Mill in 1851. Shaw & Company were still representing Lawson Mill in 1889 before closure, the manufactory being absent from the 1892 Trade Directory.

Nearby to the east was Hanover Street Mill on the west side of Kent Street, the first buildings having been erected in the early 1820s. F. & T. Sleddon were spinning cotton there in 1825, whilst Francis Sleddon, who in 1799 had started a machine shop in Bolton's Court, off Church Street, was the sole representative of Hanover Street Mill in 1828. Ambitious to enter the cotton trade,

56. A plan of Bushell Street Mill in the 1890s.

113

58. Warehouse/preparation machinery block and water tower at Bushell Street Mill, erected in the bright red brick of the 'turn of the century' period.

Sleddon had acquired building land in the Brick Croft near Stanley Street in 1801 on which he erected a workshop and a cotton factory, and in 1804 he was making machinery for this factory. In 1818, he had a machine-making business in Back Lane but in 1822 his factory blew down and in 1825 he was a bankrupt. By 1828, Sleddon had re-established himself as an iron founder in Patten Street and a cotton entrepreneur at Hanover Street Mill, where in 1832 he employed 12 spinners working hand mules. His name was still associated with Hanover Street Mill in 1844, but in 1851 the Birley Brothers were the representatives of Hanover Street Mills as spinners and manufacturers; the partnership still listed in 1892 before the mill closed, its absence noted in the 1895 Directory.

On-going extensions over the years at Hanover Street had led to a complex arrangement of buildings on the site which in 1882–83 supported 46,466 spindles and 826 looms, presenting employment for a thousand hands. The engine plant must have been of some proportions judging from the large condenser ponds to the west, whilst on the northern perimeter of the site, alongside Frank Street, stood an octagonal chimney.

From early days the site also supported a foundry and machine works, shown on Myers's Map of 1836; John Atherton, machine maker, occupied the works in 1851. The Atherton name was still associated with Hanover Street in the early 1950s by way of Atherton Bros Ltd, engineers, the firm having been established in 1835 by John Atherton in Edward Street, a move to Hanover Street being made some eight years later. By 1890, upwards of 600 hands were employed in the manufacture of winding, warping, dressing, slashing, and sizing machines as well as looms and other kinds of machinery used in cotton and linen manufacture.

Soon after its closure as a cotton factory in the early 1890s, Hanover Street Mill became a slipper-making works and later came under the ownership of the Ensign Lamp Co. Ltd.

Another Preston cotton mill whose engine data was not listed in the 1890s Assessment because of closure was Castle Street Mill, off the northern end of Moor Lane. It is mentioned as a cotton manufactory belonging to Peter Coupe in 1855 when it would have been a recent arrival, the site having supported a foundry in the 1840s when a size house and rope walk were in the immediate vicinity. In 1862, Coupe had 270 looms at Castle Street, but by the end of the decade Castle Street Mill was under the ownership of H. C. Owtram & Company who represented it in 1885–86 before closure soon afterwards, the manufactory having left the Preston lists when the 1889 Directory was published. A revised map of 1909 shows the buildings on the Castle Street Mill site as a biscuit manufactory.

Back Lane Mill and Walker Street Mill, both shown as cotton spinning factories on a large-scale map of the 1840s, had closed long before the 1890s Assessment was undertaken. Walker Street Mill was immediately north of Back Lane Mill, the latter situated at the junction of Back Lane and Great Shaw Street, off Friargate and not far from Trinity Church. Entrance to the Walker Street Mill site seems to have been from Great Shaw Street, and the trade directories do not refer to the mill by name but by address, that is, Great Shaw Street, Patten Street, or Trinity Place. Both mills were to have quite a number of entrepreneurs running them between 1828 and the time of their closure; the 1870s in the case of Back Lane Mill and the early 1880s for Walker Street Mill, the latter possibly being the one with a Great Shaw Street address belonging to James Pearson in 1818. The Back Lane site supported two firms in 1825, John Caton in spinning and John Hawkins & Co. in manufacturing. By 1828, three firms were at Back Lane Mill: Hawkins & Humber and John Hawkins, both in manufacturing, and names which would become well-known in Preston; and John Caton in spinning and manufacturing. This arrangement of three firms operating in the same premises could be yet another Preston example of the room and power system described earlier in this chapter. Such an arrangement would enable entrepreneurs like Humber & Hawkins to become established before developing their businesses on a much larger scale later in their own mills. John Caton is mentioned twice as a spinner and manufacturer in the 1828 directory, the second time with a Patten Street address which would refer to Walker Street Mill. Years later at the time of their closure, both mills were in manufacturing only.

Well over on the western side of Friargate near the canal were Edward Street and Bridge Street Mills, the former presenting some difficulty in tracing its history as it never appeared by name in the trade directories, neither did a cotton factory with that address. Scott experienced the same problem in his 1950s thesis. However, the factory is shown as a cotton mill on the 1840s map at the western end of Edward Street, on a triangular plot adjacent to what would be the Harris Technical School in the 1890s. In an Assessment of 1844, Edward Street Mill is one of four mills belonging to Paley & Company, the others being Stanley Street, Heatley Street, and Bridge Street Mills, and was probably the factory referred to as Paley's New Mill in the *Preston Chronicle* article of 19 March 1862. This lists particulars relating to number of spinners and spindles in 1832 and 1842, which for Paley's New Mill amounted to 12 spinners operating 9,024 spindles in 1832 and 11,452 spindles in 1842, all on hand mules. In 1909, the Edward Street Mill site was accommodating the Atlas Iron Works, and when Scott visited the old mill for his research, the four-storey block was still standing minus its first floor which had been removed to gain headroom by the occupiers, a firm of motor body builders.

Paley's Worsted Mill mentioned in the *Preston Chronicle* article of 1862 was Bridge Street Mill, just around the corner from Edward Street Mill, and like the latter relied on the canal for condensate cooling. Bridge Street Mill is shown as a cotton mill on Myers's Map of 1836, and presumably was the spinning and manufacturing mill listed in the 1828 Trade Directory for Samuel Haslam. Smith & Walmsley are spinning at the factory in 1855, then referred to as Bridge Mill, Marsh Lane; and at the same time, Taylor & Edington are in spinning, their address being Bridge Street. Two years later, three firms seem to be operating at the mill; William Walmsley in manufacturing, John Bailey also in manufacturing, and Smith & Walmsley in spinning. By March 1862 all of the 22 self-acting mules of Smith & Walmsley were at a standstill in the growing shadow of the Cotton Famine, even though the 66 looms of Bailey & Company were still operating six days a week. In 1865, spinners Winkfield and Walmsley have Bridge Lane for their address, and in 1869 Horrocks, Jackson & Company of Avenham Street Mills, are representing the Bridge Street factory. Soon, the mill was closed and it was demolished in the 1880s.

Diagonally opposite Bridge Street Mill and on the western side of the canal was Cable Street Mill, a spinning and weaving establishment for Oxendale & Son in 1828, who employed 16 spinners on hand mules in 1832. William Oxendale had been cotton spinning at a Pitt Street address in 1825 in what was presumably the same factory, and in 1841 Cable Street Mill was still under William and his son, but in 1844 T. Oxendale was in charge. In 1851, the Swainson brothers were the representatives followed by further changes in ownership, John Swainson being there in 1855 and Edward Hollins in 1857. In March 1862 Hollins was operating 15,480 spindles four days a week at Cable Street, whilst at his Sovereign Mill in London Road, 300 of his 754 looms lay idle. Hollins & Company were still working both mills in 1865, but for the 1869 Directory the firm and its mills are absent. By 1874, the company, now under Hollins Bros, was still at Sovereign but no longer at Cable Street, and by 1882 had taken on loomage at Peel Hall Mill. For that year the Cable Street Mill is listed for Robert Gardner & Company who had the nearby Kay Street Mill, Gardner & Company operating 11 pairs of mules and 480 looms in the Cable Street factory. About this time the firm would extend its business activities, moving into the new premises of Spa Mill, a manufactory at the northern end of Spa Road off Marsh Lane; the company's three mills employed a total of 600 hands.

In 1889, Spa Mill was the manufactory for Levi Fish, Cable Street and Kay Street Mills remaining under Gardner & Company control but for only a short time. By 1892, Cable Street Mill had left the Preston lists and Kay Street Mill had become the spinning factory for F. Mangall & Company. With company limited status by mid-decade, the factory continued in textiles as the Kay Street Cotton Spinning & Manufacturing Co. Ltd to become part of the 1896–97 'Classification of Mills for Assessment Purposes', which recorded its engine as a single McNaughted beam engine. Cylinder bores were 28″ and 38″ on respective strokes of 3′ and 6′, and horsepower on offer at 32 rpm amounted to 78; condensing facilities were met by the canal.

James Kay, cotton spinner, is mentioned in 1825 with a Bridge Lane address, and as Kay Street was just off Bridge Lane perhaps one could draw the conclusion that this refers to the new Kay Street factory, the street being named after this entrepreneur. In

1828, Gardner, Atkinson & Company were in the cotton trade with a Bridge Lane address which would be the Kay Street premises where in 1832, R. Gardner was employing 39 spinners working 43,216 spindles on hand mules, the highest spindleage at the time in a single mill in Preston.

By the mid-1850s, a second firm was operating at Kay Street: Tootal, Broadhurst & Lee, Manufacturers, who were still there in the mid-1860s before moving to Bamber Bridge, leaving Robert Gardner & Company at the Kay Street factory. Under the banner of the Kay Street Cotton Spinning & Manufacturing Co. Ltd, Kay Street Mill was part of the Preston list until it closed sometime between 1917 and 1922.

As a new manufactory of the early 1880s, Spa Mill would have started production on a horizontal engine drive, presumably the single tandem example recorded in the 1890s as having 18⅛″ and 30⅛″ bores × 4′ 6″ stroke, and offering 314 ihp at 39½ rpm. Horsepower on offer to the machinery which required 55 was 65, and actual amount being used was 60 horsepower. Boiler steam pressure was 105 psi, and weekly coal consumption was 26 tons, when the manufactory had 590 looms. Many an old photograph of the nearby Albert Edward Dock Estate shows the impressive circular chimney of Spa Mill, the base dimensions of its plinth being 17′ 6″ × 17′ 6″ from which rose the circular stalk to a height of 60 yards.

R. Gardner & Company remained at Spa Mill until at least 1885–86, but with the arrival of Levi Fish soon afterwards, the manufactory continued in the Preston lists under the Fish family name until its closure in the 1940s. Its immediate southern neighbour had been the Spindle & Ring Making Works of T. Coulthard & Company in Cooper Road, whilst to the north the Dick, Kerr Tramcar Works site of the early 1900s in Strand Road had by the early 1950s developed into the English Electric Co. Ltd Aircraft Works. When Scott visited Spa Mill at this particular time for his research, the manufactory had already become part of the aircraft works but he had the following to say about its old engine house:

> Quite the most interesting portion however, is the engine house, the floor of which is raised up 10 feet on a solid bed. The room is some 20 feet high, is oblong in plan, and contains a central row of excellently cast Doric columns, correct in detail and showing a graceful entasis, while cast iron beams support the flat roof and superimposed water-tank. The internal ceiling is very pleasantly wood panelled, and the room is well lit by tall, circular headed windows which must have made the room seem very elegant when in full operation ...

South-east of Spa Mill, to the south of Marsh Lane near Christ Church Street was Fitzroy Street Mill, a small weaving establishment seemingly opened around the early 1860s on the edge of a rural environment. In March 1862 an entrepreneur by the name of Marsden was operating 60 looms out of a total of 100, three days a week, but whilst the name of the manufactory is not listed it would be the new Fitzroy Street Mill as a Richard Marsden is listed for the same in 1865 and 1869. In 1873, Hayes & Eastwood are in charge and still there in 1880 before the arrival of Fish & Company who in Guild Year 1882 are operating 242 looms. A year later Fish had been joined by Hampson but shortly afterwards closure came, the manufactory being absent from the Trade Directory of 1885–86. No engine details have been found but one cannot overlook the possibility that Fitzroy Street Mill could have opened with one of the first horizontal engines in the Preston industry.

Not far from Fitzroy Street Mill was Arthur Street Mill, a manufactory sited just off Bow Lane, immediate to the east of the present Records office. Present on Myers's Map for 1836, it housed power looms in 1841 for Edge & Company, and was the manufactory of George Corry in 1851 who was still weaving in 1855. From then onwards there are no references by name for Arthur Street Mill and in 1873 it was the corn mill of Henry Polding, who was still there four years later. In the mid-1880s Joseph Pyke & Son were the millers, the name still associated with Arthur Street Mill in 1952. As a cotton manufactory, the mill had its two reservoirs adjacent to the street but these were to be built upon when the site underwent re-development for corn milling.

Myers's Map of 1836 shows a nucleus of cotton works in the area immediately north of Arthur Street, the majority having closed before the compiling of the 1890s Classification with the exception of one, Kay Street Mill, already mentioned.

In Ribble Street was the combined factory of Ribble Street Mill belonging to John Park & Son in 1828, and Pitt Street Mill also engaged in spinning and weaving, for Clayton & Helme who had been at the mill since at least 1825. Also in 1828 Richard Hoghton had a cotton factory in Savoy Street, and years later in 1877 in the same area near Kay Street Mill would be a manufactory for David Farnworth called Markland Street Mill, which closed in the second half of the 1880s.

On the eastern side of Bow Lane and backing onto Markland Street in 1836 was Bow Lane Mill, listed in 1825 for Miles Rodgett, spinner and manufacturer whose name was associated with the factory when it was closed in 1869. Edward Greenwood was spinning and weaving at Bow Lane Mill in 1873 and 1874 but by 1877 was in spinning only, having 12,000 spindles in 1882–83 when he employed 110 hands. Greenwood was at Bow Lane in 1885–86 but by 1889 he had left the Preston list, whilst the factory site would become the Bow Lane Iron Works.

Opposite Bow Lane Mill in 1846 was School Street at the bottom of which lay the large condenser pond of Ribble Bank Mill, a flax spinning factory at that time in nearby River Street. The factory is shown on Myers's 1836 map, and in 1869 it was the cotton spinning mill of Jacob Sellers & Son. Soon after 1874 the mill became a company limited establishment, listed in 1877 as the Ribble Bank Spinning Co. Limited, Ribble Bank Mill, River Street, G. Haworth being the managing director. In 1882–83 it was operating 31,200 spindles and had 160 hands under its employment, but closure was to come soon after the mid-1880s.

Its main five-floor block on River Street was an early example of fire-proofing in Preston, with cast-iron beam and brick vault construction plus the usual tie rods. The spinning section was separated from the preparation department by the engine house and its drive race; an early example in the town of the use of a drive race as a fire break. The boiler house was on the ground floor of the preparation block, and the entire structure minus its fifth floor was still standing when Scott visited it for his 1950s thesis, when he found a variety of businesses in occupancy including a builder; a fine art business; a Christmas card publisher; a printing firm; and a druggist partnership.

As the 1880s drew to a close it was most evident that the spinning side of the Preston cotton industry had taken an onslaught from mill fires alone from which it would never fully recover. Thomas Banks of the Spinners' Institute, an elderly spinner of sixty-seven years in the cotton industry, had cause to state in 1888 that during the previous forty years, twenty-two mills had been destroyed by fire in Preston with a total loss of spindleage amounting to some 470,898 spindles, equal to nearly 300 pairs of mules.

Mid-1862 had seen just over 27,000 looms in Preston; twelve years later a figure of 30,000 was presented, and by 1888 a figure of 35,000 was being claimed. So by the end of the 1880s a growing predominance of weaving firms had become evident in Preston, a trend that would be maintained throughout the boom period of the Edwardian age.

Some brightness amidst the doom and gloom of the 1880s had appeared in 1887 when Horrockses, Miller & Co. Ltd amalgamated with Crewdson, Crosses & Co. of Bolton and Manchester, the name of the Preston firm becoming Horrockses,

	Spindles.	Looms.	Hands employed.
Anderton, John, Grimshaw-street	—	717	290
Arkwright, Daniel, Hawkins-street	36,248	599	650
Aspden, Richard and Co., Bamber Bridge..	—	240	102
Birley, Beaumont, and Co., Isherwood-st.	27,160	—	110
Birley, Bros., Hanover-street	46,466	826	1,000
Bashall, Wm. and Co., Farington	50,088	708	750
Bourne, J. and W., Brindle Mill	30,000	330	276
Brazill, W., Great Shaw-street (stopped) ..	—	230	—
Brindle, T. and Co., New Hall-lane	—	1,080	620
Brotherton and Co, Hunt-street	—	558	270
Calvert, William and Sons, Preston and Walton-le-Dale	151,146	2,544	2,218
Catterall, Paul, Son, and Co., Rigby-st.	41,600	—	210
Cockshutt, J., Walton-le-Dale	25,000	—	70
Copland, M. B., Pole-street	27,800	—	104
Crewdson and Grierson, Walmer Bridge ..	—	500	280
Dewhurst Geo. and R., Higher Walton and Cuerden Mill	145,488	2,185	2,030
Eccles, J. and Co., Fylde-road	—	600	300
Eccles, Thos., Sons, and Co., School-lane..	49,286	824	600
Eccles Brothers, New Hall Mill, Wellington Mill, and Victoria Mill	90,360	1,073	730
Eccles, William and Son, Bamber Bridge..	30,000	476	413
Fylde-road Spinning Co. (Nimmo, W.), Water-lane	30,000	—	160
Fylde Manufacturing Co., Kirkham	—	540	270
Gardner, R. and Co., Kay-street, Cable-street, and Spa-road	48,392	900	600
Goodair, J. and Co., Brookfield-street, Lambert's-bottoms, and Fletcher's-road	73,524	1,322	1,120
Goodair, R., Brook-street	—	576	320
Greenwood, Edward, Bow-lane	12,000	—	110
Hampson and Fish, Fitzroy-street, Upper James-street, and Deepdale-Mill-street..	—	1,559	835
Harrison, W., Kirkham	30,000	—	130
Hartford Mills Co., Limited, Campbell-st.	44,064	503	420
Hartley, Bros., Shelley-road	41,288	866	650
Haslam, J and J., Parker-street	41,328	—	154
Hawkins, John and Sons, Adelphi-street and St. Paul's-road	95,502	1,926	1,581
Hayhurst and Marsden, Longridge	6,500	405	200
Hayes, Edward, Markland-street	—	240	100
Healey. E.. Brook-street	—	684	420
Hincksman, W. H., Croft-street	36,128	—	170
Hollins, Bros. and Co., London-road and Fletcher's-road	—	1,130	535
Hopkins, Martin, and Co., St. Paul's-road..	—	340	150
Horrocks, Jacson, and Co., Avenham-street	53,000	70	200
Horrockses, Miller, and Co., Stanley-street (Yard Works) and New Hall-lane	150,000	3,100	3,000
Humber, J. junr., Bushell-street	46,000	642	570
Leese, S. and E., Fylde-road	40,000	400	363
Leigh, J. and A., Old Lancaster-lane	40,720	1,156	1,000
Liver, J. and Co., Peel Hall-street	—	475	220
Livesey, T., Moor Brook-street	—	645	270
Longridge Manufacturing Co., Longridge.	—	475	240
Lostock Hall Spinning Co., Lostock Hall	55,000	—	160
Maynard, M. S., Bold-street	42,000	—	130
Mc.Guffog, T. and W., Murray-street	43,396	—	180
Mellor, Bros., George-street	30,000	—	104
Moor Park Manufacturing Co. (Limited), St. George's-road	—	489	224
Orr, J and A. S., School-lane, Higher Walton	3,400	579	359
Owtram, H. C. and Co, Mosley-street and Castle-street	—	1,260	546
Oxhey Spinning and Manufacturing Co. (Limited), Ripon-street	18,086	318	260
Paley, Wm., Hopwood street, Primrose Hill, and Bank-top, Fishwick	32,000	704	460
Park Mills Spinning Co., North-road	43,900	—	240
Pilkington and Berry, Mount Pleasant Mill and Earnshaw Bridge Mill, Leyland	6,600	676	425
Preston Spinning and Manufacturing Co. (Limited), Wellfield-road	49,650	752	700
Reade and Wall, Brook Mills, Leyland	—	600	500
Ribble Bank Spinning Co. (Limited), River-street	31,200	—	160
Richards Brothers, Freckleton-st., Kirkham	—	168	98
Richards, Bowdler, and Co., Wesham Mills, Kirkham	65,406	—	270
Shaw, William and Co., Cumberland-street	—	425	190
Simpson, L. and Co., Park Mill-court, North-road	—	868	400
Simpson and Jackson, Gregson-lane, Higher Walton	31,000	216	230
Smalley, John, Pitt-street	—	413	200
Smith, S. and Co (R. Grime), Kent-street	28,688	520	350
Smith, J., Southgate and Ribbleton	62,860	1,061	1,020
Smith, W. and Co., Green Bank-street	—	750	350
Smith, Robert, Longridge	—	540	320
Sowerbutts, W. and H. E., Freckleton	—	500	300
Swainson, Birley, and Co., Fishwick	97,278	1,422	1,600
Tennyson-road Spinning and Manufacturing Co. (Limited), Tennyson-road	—	344	200
Wade, Jas., Fylde-road	—	226	80
Walmsley, B., Lord-street	12,000	—	50
Walker, Moss and Co., Kirkham	—	1,142	600
Walsh, Richard and Co., Ashton-on-Ribble	—	400	160
Whitle, Geo. and Co, Longridge	—	584	320
Wilding, Bros., Skeffington-road	—	927	530
Woods, J. F., Cemetery-road	—	450	250
Woods, Hampson, and Co, Croston	—	460	300

The totals of the foregoing figures are—spindles, 2,191,552; looms, 48,243 hands employed, 36,977.

59. A list of master cotton spinners and manufacturers in Preston and district, 1882–83.

Crewdson & Co. Ltd. Much expansion and modernisation had taken place at the firm's Yard Works over the years, one 1880s introduction being a weaving shed for 1,000 looms in Guild Year, 1882. It would be in the building of Centenary Mill in the opening years of the next decade that the new company would arrange for one of the most impressive engine installations in Preston.

CHAPTER EIGHT

The 1890s

To celebrate a century of textiles and to extend their spinning facilities, Horrockses, Crewdson & Co. Ltd went ahead in the first half of the 1890s with the erection of Centenary Mill at the western end of New Hall Lane on a site that had once housed the early hand-loom workshops of the firm's founder, John Horrocks. The new spinning mill would cost approximately £125,000 to build and equip, and whilst it is not listed in the Trade Directory for 1895, it would be in production in that year, its ledger accounts showing a large increase in expenses from May to November, the following figures being to the nearest pound.

May 31st, 1895 (expenses)

Cotton £7,744; coal £350; gas and water £58; oil and tallow £112; insurance £15; wages £1,439.

November 30th, 1895 (expenses)

Cotton £43,854; coal £582; gas and water £104; oil and tallow £123; insurance £162; wages £5,646.

Among the accounts, valuation figures for 31 May 1896 were given to the nearest pound:

Land required for New Spinning Mill £3,045

New Spinning Mill brickworks (including engine house

and boiler house) £46,747

Cost of making reservoirs £5,119

Steam engines £7,281

Boilers and economisers £3,209

Mill gearing £3,814

Electric installation £1,832

Machinery (spinning) £55,289

Steam and gas piping £508

Utensils (spinning) £3,767

Sprinkler installation £1,483

Paving £16

Centenary was one of the first mills in Lancashire to have rolled

60. Centenary Mill.
(Harris Museum, Preston)

steel beams and concrete floors, and its main staircase tower had an open loggia executed in an Italianate style. The engine chosen for the new mill was a horizontal four cylinder triple expansion example by John Musgrave & Sons of the Globe Iron Works, Bolton. Cylinder layout consisted of a high pressure cylinder and a low pressure one in tandem driving one crank, and an intermediate pressure cylinder in tandem with another low pressure cylinder driving the opposite crank. Cylinders bores were 24¼″, 36″, 40″ and 40″ on a 6′ stroke for an engine designed for approximately 2,000 horsepower.

In the four cylinder triple expansion engine, steam was first expanded in a high pressure cylinder, then an intermediate pressure one before being divided, each half undergoing final expansion in its own low pressure cylinder. By using two moderately sized cylinders for the third expansion stage instead of one huge cylinder, bore diameters could be kept to a sensible size to allow ease of transportation of cylinders from works to mill. Also, piston weights could be kept to a reasonable figure, important when considering wear on cylinders and pistons. Cranks of these engines were set quartering for easy starting in any position of the engines, and all working parts of the well-balanced cylinder layout were easily accessible. Four cylinder triples were most economic prime movers and a popular choice for large drive in Lancashire mills throughout the 1890s and early 1900s.

Another form of horizontal engine to be adopted for large mill drive was the twin tandem compound, made up of two identical engines, one on either side of the driving drum and comprising a high and a low pressure cylinder in tandem. Such a layout provided even driving, essential for spinning, and one virtue of this type of engine was that if one side broke down, the other engine could continue to drive the mill, even if it were to be on a part-loading arrangement until repairs were completed, thus avoiding a total shutdown of the mill.

However, it would seem the twin tandem compound type would not grace the Preston scene. If it had, most likely its debut would have been at Centenary; the period was appropriate, the new mill

61. The engine house at Centenary Mill. Left is the ground-floor extension of the preparatory section, and to the right of the engine house is the square chimney of New Preston Mill.

62. The Musgrave four-cylinder triple-expansion engine at Centenary Mill. On the right is the high-pressure cylinder, while on the left is the intermediate pressure cylinder. Behind, in tandem with each cylinder, is a low-pressure cylinder.

a worthy size for such an engine. In 1890, Musgraves had fitted one of 1,800 horsepower to replace a beam engine drive at India Mill, Darwen.

As well as providing rope drive, the engine at Centenary Mill also ran an alternator for general lighting. The absence of electricity charges in the accounts of 1895 and the valuation figure for electric installation for May 1896 are firm indicators that electricity was produced via mill engine and alternator for lighting from the outset.

One employee remembered that five minutes before shutdown at the end of a working day, with the mill engine slowing down and its alternator power fading, a Belliss-Morcom steam set coupled to generator and switch panel was brought into action to provide pilot lighting for workers leaving the mill. Charges for gas as listed in the expense accounts for 1895 would be in connection with a process known as 'gassing' in which a gas flame was applied to the cotton thread to singe off excess fibres, so producing a smoother yarn.

As was common to a large spinning mill, Centenary had a rear extension to its ground floor preparation department, and in the entrance yard stood its impressive chimney, a circular one of 18 feet base diameter rising from a square plinth to a height of 63 yards.

For smaller power drives such as in weaving, one form of horizontal engine adopting the triple expansion of steam was the semi-tandem. On one crank would be a high pressure cylinder in tandem with an intermediate pressure cylinder, whilst on the opposite crank would be the low pressure cylinder in tandem with the engine's condenser. Oakbank Mill in Nelson had a Pollitt

& Wigzell example of 1897, whilst Hendon Shed next door had one made by William Roberts & Company in 1900. However, the semi-tandem type seemingly did not appear in Preston.

As well as the tandem triple at Bank Top Mill mentioned in Chapter 6, and the Centenary engine, another engine operating on the triple expansion principle in Preston during the 1890s was the beam engine at Kent Street Mill. Cylinder bores were 16″, 22″ and 30″ on respective strokes of 2′ 6″, 3′ 4″, and 5′. With corresponding average pressures at 54 psi, 16 psi, and 4.5 psi, respective ihps being generated were 57, 41.7, and 37.8 at 38 rpm. Horsepower available for machinery amounted to 83 of which 42 was being taken for a requirement of 41.

At this particular time, Kent Street Mill was a manufactory with 468 dobbies, in contrast to some years previously when it had been a combined enterprise with mule spindles, throstle spindles, and loomage. Listed in the 1890s was a small vertical engine with a 6″ diameter high pressure cylinder and a 10″ diameter low pressure one, driving two taping machines.

In 1891, Fosters had made a boiler for 160 psi pressure and it would be about this time when the triple expansion beam engine came about, most probably arising from a design scheme by J. H. Tattersall, a Preston consulting engineer who during the 1890s was well known for his work on triple expansion beam engines. To his designs, Buckley & Taylor at their Castle Iron Works, Greenacres, Oldham, were to begin a revival of beam engine building in the 1890s, their first triple expansion example being for a Chorley Mill in 1895. At least eleven more engines to Tattersall's designs were constructed by the Oldham firm between 1895 and 1904, the largest being the two built in 1899, one for the Nile Mill in Chadderton and the other for the Tay Mill in Oldham. Rated at 2,500 ihp each, these double version engines were the most powerful beam engines to be installed in a cotton mill.

The Kent Street triple was most probably a modification of its old beam engine, quite possibly a single, McNaughted example to be altered by the addition of a new high pressure cylinder fitted between crankshaft and column, with the intermediate and low pressure cylinders on the other side of the column as in the Nile engines.

Kent Street Mill, although absent on the 1844–47 Ordnance Survey Map, was occupied by Slater & Smith, cotton spinners and manufacturers in 1851. By 1860, Goodair had joined the firm but his name is absent for the mill in 1865 when Slater & Smith are still its representatives. Smith & Co. are in charge in 1869, the Smith name being still associated with the factory in the early

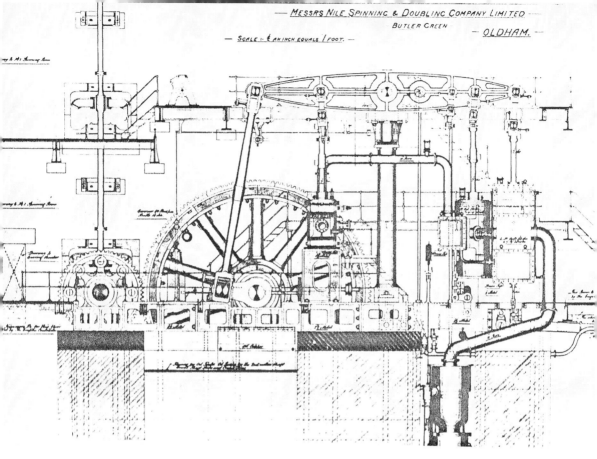

63. An illustration of one side of one pair of a triple-expansion beam engine designed by J. H. Tattersall of Preston and built by Buckley & Taylor of Oldham for the Nile Mill, Chadderton, Oldham, in 1899. The Kent Street mill engine, Preston, although a single-engine example, must have been similar in design.

1880s when it housed 25,000 spindles on mules, 3,100 spindles on throstles, and 510 looms. Business had changed to weaving only by 1885–86 when Cecil Woodmass represented the manufactory, which is absent from the Preston lists for 1889, most likely due to a shutdown period awaiting new ownership followed by modernisation of boiler and engine plant, as John Liver & Co. are manufacturing there in 1892. By the mid-1890s, John Liver was at Brookfield Mill, and James W. Liver in charge at Kent Street, but a further change in ownership had come about by 1901 when Bibby & Burton Ltd are at the Kent Street manufactory, to be followed by Burton & Frost Ltd, who are listed for 1904. The latter are still the representatives in 1917 but in 1922 Kent Street Mill was under George Burton Ltd, continuing in that name until final closure came in the second half of the 1960s.

Frenchwood Mill, sited alongside what would be James Street, off London Road, had been built for John Horrocks in the 1790s, and in 1832 it was the factory for Horrockses, Miller & Co. who employed twelve spinners on hand mules. It was still operating under the same company in 1874 but thereafter the title, Frenchwood Mill, is not mentioned in trade directory listing until 1892 when it is the manufactory for Seymour Redmayne. It would seem that as far back as 1869 a part of the factory was a manufactory for Woods & Hampson going under the name of Swillbrook Mill, its address being James Street, this weaving business continuing long after Horrockses, Miller & Co. had left. Hampson, Smith & Co. have 782 looms there in 1882, a figure which almost tallies with that of 780 given in the 1890s Classification, when the looms were mostly dobbies. By 1883 the manufactory is under Hampson & Fish Ltd and likewise in 1889, but in 1892 it is listed as Frenchwood Mill, James Street south for Seymour Redmayne, and in 1895 as the Frenchwood Mill Company.

Its engine listed in the Classification for 1897 is quoted as a compound horizontal with 20″ and 36 5⁄16″ bores, average working pressures being 31.5 psi and 12 psi respectively to give corresponding ihps of 138 and 71 at 38 rpm. Horsepower on offer was 99 to machinery requiring 64, and at this time the manufactory had two boilers by Galloway for 65 psi pressure.

Weaving continued at Frenchwood Mill for years afterwards, Bibby & Burton Ltd being listed for 1901; Brierley, Bentley, Adams & Craig Ltd for the Directories of 1904 and 1907. In 1913 the manufactory is operating under the title of the Frenchwood Mill Co. Ltd, closure taking place eventually sometime between 1927 and 1932.

One of the largest of cotton mill sites in the Preston District in the 1890s was William Calvert & Sons' Flats Mills on the outskirts in Walton-le-Dale, where four main drive engines were in operation, with a fifth one to be on order around the end of the decade.

The first phase of this multi-mill layout site had appeared by the 1820s, William Calvert (1787–1861) being listed in a Trade Directory of 1825 as 'Cotton manufacturer, Walton-le-Dale', the business beginning with hand looms. In 1838, the firm's number one mill would receive a single cylinder beam engine to be McNaughted later, the name of Musgraves of Bolton being associated with it. In the 1890s this engine is listed as having 36″ and 42″ bores on respective strokes of 3′ and 6′. Average pressures were 33.9 and 10.4 psi to give corresponding ihps of 225 and 188 at 36 rpm.

For number two mill, Musgraves would provide a large single tandem compound in Guild Year, 1882, its general dimensions of 31″ and 52″ bores × 6′ stroke being the same as the single tandem at Calvert's Aqueduct Street in Preston, mentioned in chapter seven. Respective average working pressures of the Flats 1882 engine were 32.4 and 11.5 psi to bring about corresponding ihps of 400 and 400 at 45 rpm.

Mill number three was engined by a vertical compound type,

new in 1892, which had 25″ and 44″ bores × 3′ 6″ stroke, indicating respective ihps of 324 and 260 for corresponding average pressures of 38.9 and 10 psi at 80 rpm. Most probably this would be a Musgrave engine of the single crank type, similar to the Yates example of the 1880s at Wellington Mill mentioned in chapter seven.

For number four mill, new in the 1890s, a horizontal compound was installed having 22″ and 33″ bores × 4′ 6″ stroke, which at 50 rpm developed respective ihps of 160 and 100 for corresponding average pressures of 31 and 8.5 psi.

From this aggregate of 2,057 indicated horsepower from the four engines, only 616 horsepower was available to the machinery, the culprit for such a loss of power from engines to machines being geared drive transmission. The 1890s Classification for Flats Mills mentions a large amount of gearing from mill to mill and

64. A Musgrave single-crank vertical compound engine with triangular connecting rod. The engine shown must have been identical to the one installed by the Bolton firm of engine builders in Flats Mill, Walton-le-Dale, in c. 1899.

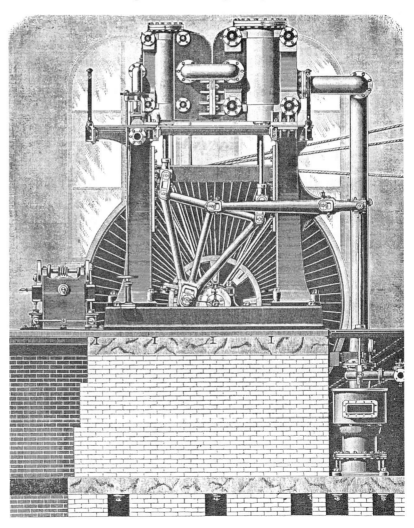

also a great loss in pressure (i.e. steam pressure from boilers to engines) by distance from boilers.

Nine boilers were in situ, five having been made by Adamson in 1885 which were steaming at 95 psi pressure, and the other four built by Stevensons in 1872 which were contributing a pressure of 75psi. Most likely the 60-yard circular chimney had been built for one of these boiler sets, but soon after the mid-1890s a second circular chimney would appear along with a new engine and engine house, this addition of motive power providing drive for a new weaving shed housing some 2,000 looms.

Built in c. 1899 by Musgraves, the new engine would be of the single crank vertical compound type with the triangular connecting rod patent of Fleming & Ferguson as mentioned in chapter seven. Musgraves adopted such a design patent on their vertical engines for compound, triple expansion, and quadruple expansion working during a particular period of their engine manufacturing activities. Little data has come to light in connection with the new vertical engine at Flats except the mention of 24″ and 50″ bores × 4′ stroke. A visit to its engine house in the 1970s found the building which had been erected in the bright red brick of the turn of the century period, deserted and empty, many years having passed since the removal of its fine engine.

In 1882–83 Flats Mills had the highest mule spindleage on a single site in the Preston District with 151,146 spindles, and supported 2,544 looms. Equally impressive would be the new weaving extensions of two decades later, but closure would come in 1931 due to company failure. The new sheds eventually became a wine store whilst most of the mill site was taken over by the Ribble Paper Mills Ltd when the new turn of the century engine house would accommodate paper pulping machinery.

The compact design of the vertical compound engine made it a most suitable replacement unit to an ageing beam engine without the necessity of erecting a new engine house. This was to be the case at Brookhouse Mills in the second half of the 1890s when in 1896, Yates & Thom were to build a cross compound version as a replacement to the pair of McNaughted beam engines driving mills one and two. The new engine of 750 horsepower had 18″ and 48″ bores × 4′ 6″ stroke and ran at 80 rpm.

As the twentieth century approached, the Preston industry, now reasonably equipped with quite a number of up-to-date power plants (although in many of its mills antiquated engines were at work), was in readiness for the demands of a textile industry that would have its final impact on the Lancashire scene before the outbreak of the Great War.

CHAPTER NINE

'The Golden Autumn': 1900 to The Great War

I N 1894, Preston had conceded her fourth position in the spinning town rankings to Stockport where in the previous year the largest ring spinning mill in the Lancashire industry had been built. As the new century approached, a trade boom in Lancashire textiles lasted from 1898 until 1901, followed by another in 1905–07, each one heralding a county-wide building programme of new spinning company limited mills and manufactories. Such a trend continued after 1907 albeit at a slower rate until halted by the outbreak of war in 1914. This period in Lancashire textiles has been aptly referred to as 'Cotton's Golden Autumn', its Indian summer before the harsh winter of its final demise.

In Preston, a wave of new textile factory construction began to gain momentum on 1 November 1900, when Horrockses, Crewdson & Co. Ltd purchased the old Fishwick Mill of Swainson & Birley, off London Road, with the intention of demolishing it to make way for a new weaving mill.

John Swainson had been the proprietor of Willow Street Mill at the corner of Leeming Street and Willow Street in 1823 and also ran a machine shop in Willow Street. In 1826 Swainson went into partnership with Birley & Turton, opening a new cotton mill at Fishwick to be known as 'The Big Factory' because of its huge proportions. The mill is listed under Cotton Spinners and Manufacturers in the 1828 Directory, and is represented by Swainson, Birley & Co. in 1832 when it housed 26,640 spindles on hand mules, the third highest spindleage in a single mill in Preston at that time. Under the same ownership in 1862, it had 62,000 spindles, all on self actors, and 1,420 looms, and by 1882–83 its spindleage had reached a figure of 97,278, and with 1,422 looms, it employed 1,600 hands.

About this time the factory received a Blackburn-built engine; an entry of 7 August 1882, in Yates's Book of Engine Lists (1876–84) mentions 'Compound Horizontal Engine with cylinders side by side for Messrs Swainson, Birley & Co., Preston.' Cylinder bores were 19″ and 34″ × 4′ 6″ stroke, and the engine was fitted with McNaught & Varley valves. Engine speed would be 55 rpm, and the spur flywheel for geared drive was 10′ 5⅞″ in diameter × 13″ in width and had 80 cogs at 4½″ pitch. The spur pinion wheel had 46 cogs and was 5′ 5¹³⁄₁₆″ in diameter, whilst the air pump had a 22″ bore × 20″ stroke and the condenser was 30″ diameter × 4′ 10½″ high.

Yates's had done some engine work for Swainson, Birley & Co. in 1873, one entry for that year in the Blackburn firm's Book of Engine Lists recording 'Alteration of Nos 5 and 7 engines'. Another entry for the same year lists an engine with 23″ and 43″ bores × 5′ stroke, the high pressure cylinder having cut-off slide valves. Designed for a speed of 40 rpm, the engine had a spur flywheel with 168 cogs and the connecting rods were 13′ 6″ long.

Horizontal engines at Fishwick Mill would have been used for driving looms and associated preparatory work, and for some processes in the dye works section. For the spinning side, a beam engine drive would have been in operation, that is up to c. 1892, the year when the same Blackburn engine firm, then Yates & Thom made a vertical compound engine for Fishwick Mills. This engine was to be given a new lease of life in the rebuilding programme at Fishwick, and the mill's Private Ledger for 1901–05, now in the Lancashire Record Office, reveals interesting information regarding such and the building activity in general.

For 31 May 1901 an entry in the ledger records that the purchase price for the old buildings plus sundries came to just over £5,572, with the boilers and economisers listed at £1,500 and reservoir water rights costing £2,000.

Prior to demolition the factory site had consisted basically of a mill block with projecting engine house on its northern side, and a boiler house some distance away at the western end, near a weaving shed which had its own engine house. In front of the mill was the dye works section with two engine houses adjacent to one another and next to a boiler house; one engine operating a pump over an artesian well whilst the other one presumably provided general drive.

Building construction was well under way by 1902 at what was termed the West End, that is where the mill block had been and where the boiler house with boilers and economisers would be spared demolition. Salmon Street was diverted in 1903 on account of the new layout, and by April 1905, the new weaving complex was valued at just over £83,000. In October its electrical installation had a value of £596, a figure which had reached £1,880 twelve months later.

'The Golden Autumn': 1900 to The Great War

On completion the weaving mill and dyeworks were impressive, each having been built in bright red machine-made brick which was seen to good effect in the high, panelled boundary walls, contrasting sharply with two old brick chimneys which had been left. One was an octagonal example of about 50 yards in height on the western end, the other a square one of 63 yards to the east of it.

The price for the Longridge stone used for lintels, coping, moulded string courses and so on was listed in 1904 when two engine houses were built, a large one at the West End and one of smaller dimensions in the dye works section. An entry for 31 October 1904 in the Private Ledger for the dye works lists engines and gearing worth £898; machinery at almost £3,748; and electrical installation at nearly £86. The steam pumping engine there would be replaced in the 1930s by a 50-horsepower motor.

However, it was the entry in the Ledger for April 1905, for the West End which mentions new engines and gearing valued at £3,172, that would arouse considerable interest as to the identity of the power plant after noting the tallness and length of the new engine house of 1904. Such dimensions were in keeping with an engine house for a multi-storey spinning mill of the period and not as would be the case at Fishwick, a weaving shed layout.

Scott, for his 1952 thesis, had visited the engine house and seen its engine, later writing:

> The only notable feature of Fishwick Mill is the engine house, which was built about 40 feet high, to accommodate the huge vertical beam engine, moved en bloc from the Old Swainson & Birley's Mill. The engine itself, is very impressive ...

What Scott had seen was not a beam engine but a vertical cross compound one, the identity of which would later be confirmed. A visit to the engine house (which then housed an oil-fired boiler plant) in 1978 to enquire about the identity of its former engine drew a blank. Shortly afterwards, two letters were to shed light on the subject, and years later I came into the possession of a photograph of the engine.

The first of these correspondences came from the late George Watkins of Bristol, who had also taken the photograph, and whose publications on stationary engines are a must for steam power enthusiasts. Having visited Fishwick Mill when the engine was still in situ, he was able to send a description and details of it as being a vertical compound, made in 1892, having 24″ and 48″ bores × 5′ stroke, driving a weaving shed. The second letter arrived shortly afterwards from the late Edward Hanson of the Northern Mill Engine Society, who mentioned a Yates & Thom vertical cross compound, made in 1892 with 24″ and 48″ bores × 5′ stroke, which had run at 64 rpm, belonging to Horrockses.

This information and the photograph, along with Scott's comment, served to explain what had happened at Fishwick during the rebuilding programme, In 1898, Fishwick Mills were still operational for Swainson, Birley & Co., and when closure came, the new vertical engine of 1892, which presumably had been fitted in the projecting engine house on the old mill block, was dismantled to be re-assembled in the engine house of 1904. The reason for the substantial length of the new engine house was to accommodate rope drive to a first motion shaft, which ran alongside the northern flank of the new weaving shed in a covered alleyway.

The engine, shown in this chapter, had Corliss valves and was capable of about 1,000 horsepower, and most likely drove an alternator for the electrical installation. The photograph shows the flywheel providing rope drive to a large pulley on the first motion shaft which runs across the centre of the scene. Above the flywheel are the high and low pressure cylinders, the photograph clearly indicating the height dimension associated with a vertical compound engine.

Swainson's Willow Street Mill was a factory which would present little information about his history. It appears in the 1816 Directory, and for the Directory of 1818 three firms are represented in Willow Street: William Lancaster; Swainsons & Company; and Swainson & Thorp. Presumably all three were on the same site, as Tulket's description of Willow Street Mill in 1821 presents a factory complex of some proportions. William Davis & Co., spinners and manufacturers, are at the mill in 1828 when George Smith & Son are manufacturing with a Leeming Street address, again presumably the Willow Street factory as Leeming Street ran on its western side and eventually became Manchester Road.

Josiah Barker is spinning and manufacturing in Leeming Street in 1841, whilst S. L. Behren has power looms there and James Hogg is working hand looms. Myers's large scale map of 1846 shows Willow Street Mill, with its reservoir boundary wall in Grimshaw Street, but after the 1840s no reference to the mill is to be found in the mill lists of the trade directories. The Guardian Map of 1865 shows the mill site supporting a tiny reservoir and much-altered and reduced buildings. Nearly a century later at the beginning of the 1950s, the site was accommodating a food warehouse.

The site plan in the 1890s Classification for the Yard Works of Horrockses, Crewdson Co. Ltd, shows five engine houses: the Dale Street one; the Guild Merchant; one erected in 1836; one

65. Mills to the east of London Road, looking north-east. Bank Top Mill is at centre, while behind can be seen the tall engine house of 1904 for the new weaving complex of Horrockses, Crewdson & Co. Ltd, Fishwick Mill, the weaving shed lying opposite the dye works section on the right of the photograph. North of Fishwick Mill is the multi-storey block with mansard roof of Primrose Mill, near New Hall Lane Mill, which is at the top of the photograph.

raised in 1845; and a fifth one near the western boundary, complete with rope race passage and within which a new engine was then being installed. Unfortunately no engine details were recorded for any of these engine houses in the Classification.

However, a company employee interviewed in the 1970s recalled the Guild Merchant engine as having steel band drive, its flywheel and first motion shaft pulley faced with cork.

This form of drive, which apparently had evolved from a German patent, was introduced in the 1890s and enjoyed some popularity for mill drive between 1910 and 1920. The bands, or belts as they were sometimes referred to, were jointed in situ, the band tensioned with clamps drawn together before the lap joint was brazed. If a band began to slip due to the cork covering becoming polished, the grip was re-established by using a brush handle, around the end of which was wrapped fine glasspaper, which was passed along the cork surface whilst it was in motion.

Yard Works in Stanley Street was in 1900 the largest concentration of cotton works in Preston and district, and in that year amongst a dense collection of mill blocks and weaving sheds an engine house was erected on the north-western corner of Field Mill. Drive from the new engine, whose make and statistics are unknown, ran in an annex rope race built on the end wall of the mill. Glass panelled, the race ran to several storeys in height allowing a system of ropes to drive succeeding levels of longitudinal shafting which previously would have been driven by geared drive, presumably from the engine house of 1836 at the opposite end of the mill block. A site model of Yard Works in Preston's Harris Museum shows the Field Mill race and two

66. Engine house at the Fishwick Mill of Horrockses, Crewdson & Co. Ltd. Its tall proportions were to accommodate a re-assembled vertical cross-compound engine, made in 1892 by Yates & Thom of Blackburn for the old Fishwick Mill of Swainson & Birley.

67. The Yates & Thom vertical cross-compound of 1892 in its new engine house of 1904 at Fishwick Mill. Top right is the high-pressure cylinder, while top left is the low-pressure one. Rope drive is to a large pulley wheel on the first motion shaft which runs across the centre of this photograph which was taken in 1960.

'The Golden Autumn': 1900 to The Great War

68. Yard Works: an aerial view looking north-east.

69 (*opposite, bottom*). A model of the Yard Works site in the Harris Museum, Preston, showing Field Mill in the centre with annex rope race on its western gable. The engine house of 1900 is on the left.

70 (*below*). Another detail of the same model. In the centre, alongside the chimney, is the 1915 engine house which would house the Hick, Hargreaves cross-compound engine.

more about the site. The adoption of annex drive races as at Yard Works were not uncommon in Lancashire during this period when a changeover from geared to rope drive had to be met.

In 1915, another engine house had appeared at Yard Works, this time alongside the 1836 engine house, for a 2,000 horsepower horizontal cross compound engine made in 1915 by Hick, Hargreaves & Co. Ltd of Soho Foundry, Bolton. It was their Works No. 715, and with bores of 30″ and 60″ × 5′ stroke, the engines named 'King' and 'Queen' would drive a 25′ diameter flywheel at 65 rpm. The 46-rope drive was divided with most of the ropes going to a mill shaft, whilst others in driving to the rear attended an alternator which supplied power to motors in another section. At one end of the engine house the uppermost ropes ran across a yardway through a wooden bridge, whilst the bottom ropes ran underground. Steam supply to the engine was at 180 psi pressure. A drawing dated March 1923 of the Field Mill boiler house shows seven boilers which were serving the Dale Street engine, the 1900 engine, the 1915 engine, and a Belliss engine.

The slashing department which was driven for most of the day by an alternator running off a steam engine had to continue working throughout the lunch break. So when the steam engine

71. The Hick, Hargreaves engine of 1915 at Yard Works.

began to slow down for its lunchtime stoppage, power to the slashing department was synchronised from the alternator with the town supply; the procedure being reversed at the end of the lunchtime break.

At the firm's nearby New Preston Mills, a horizontal single tandem drove a weaving section, the drive shaft running across an open yard into the shed, whilst for the mill an inverted vertical triple expansion engine provided rope drive.

The inverted vertical triple, often referred to as a marine triple because of its popularity in ship propulsion at this time, had its three vertical cylinders, that is high, intermediate and low pressure, positioned in direct alignment above a common crankshaft, at one end of which was the driving drum. Such an arrangement provided a compact power unit which allowed reasonable access to the working parts for cleaning and general maintenance. High revolutions could be achieved using the short stroke of the marine triple which would become a popular choice for textile mill drive from 1900 onwards.

Yates & Thom were to build one in 1902 to replace the Hicks double McNaughted beam engine which had been driving the 1860 mill at the Higher Walton Mills of G. & R. Dewhurst. The new triple, installed in a new engine house on the end of the mill block, was also to drive an alternator. Bores were 20″, 32″ and 51″ × 4′ 6″ stroke, and at 71 rpm, 1150 to 1250 horsepower was met on a steam pressure of 170 psi.

Another engine to arrive at the Higher Walton factory was a horizontal single tandem recalled as having 15″ and 29″ bores × 2½′ stroke, made in 1908 to produce 330 horsepower. It was

72. Two photographs of the Higher Walton Mills of G. and R. Dewhurst, which in 1932 became the factory of the Lancashire Cotton Corporation, and in 1937 the workplace of the Preston Tyre Fabric Manufacturing Company. The lower photograph shows the new engine house for the Yates & Thoms 'marine type' inverted vertical triple-expansion engine of 1902 on the end of the 1860 mill block.

141

fitted in a new engine house alongside a weaving shed for which
it provided drive, presumably replacing the old double
McNaughted beam engine, compounded in 1877 by Yates as
mentioned in chapter four.

The Dewhurst name continued at Higher Walton until 1932
when the factory was bought by the Lancashire Cotton
Corporation who had it until 1937 when the Preston Tyre Fabric
Manufacturing Company Limited took over to specialise in cord
fabrics for tyres, belting, hoses and heavy canvas.

In 1910, G. & R. Dewhurst Ltd were also working Cuerden
and Farington mills to the south of Preston, and Arkwright Mill
in Preston. Up to 1916, the mill and sheds at Arkwright Mill,
which was still a Dewhurst factory at the time, had been driven
by gearing from the double McNaughted beam engine mentioned
in chapter four. About this time, Cole, Marchent & Morley of
Prospect Foundry, Bradford were to replace the engine with an
inverted vertical triple which had 23 ¾″, 35″ and 56″ bores × 3′
stroke, and ran at 98½ rpm to develop 1,500 horsepower. Its
drop piston valves enabled the engine to use highly superheated
steam at 500°F and 160–180 psi pressure, provided by a bank of
four boilers supplied by Tinker, Shenton & Co. of Hyde; three
in use, one on standby. Five floors of the mill were driven by
ropes from the 17′ diameter flywheel which had 21 grooves for
1½″ diameter ropes; the weaving shed being driven by bevel
gearing and shafting from the extended flywheel shaft.

The triple also drove two dynamos by a system of pulleys and
ropes from the flywheel shaft, the dynamos generating 220–230
volts for lighting and positioned where the beam engine had been.
There was the usual changeover switch for town supply up to
7.30 a.m. before the triple took over, and it was arranged for the
sizing process to run continuously throughout the day on town
supply, this continuing operating being essential to avoid the sized
yarn sticking to the machinery.

Arkwright Mill also had a standby steam set by way of a
vertical, twin cylinder Belliss-Morcom engine. During the summer
months the Bradford-built main engine could be temperamental
for a morning start if a loss in vacuum had occurred due to
condenser cooling water not having cooled sufficiently overnight
in the reservoir. Such a loss encouraged a build-up of steam in
the low pressure cylinder so counteracting some of the driving
power of the incoming steam for the working stroke, and
only after cold town water had been flooded into the engine
condenser by a pump would the Arkwright triple begin to achieve
its working vacuum of 23″ to 24″. The new engine house had
been an extension of the old one, and one interesting feature in

the new engine room was the owner's monogram, 'GRD', in the tiling.

One may ask why a Bradford-built engine was chosen when Preston had so many engine firms nearby. At this particular period many of these local firms would be engaged on war work, but it must be stressed that Cole, Marchent & Morley, established 1848, were first-class engine builders and may well have secured the tender to engine Arkwright from among a number of strong contenders. The Bradford firm was well known in Preston for its engineering expertise having provided two compound engines to drive the Dick, Kerr multipolar generators of Preston Corporation Electric Tramways which had begun operations on 7 June 1904.

The new spinning mills erected between 1900 and 1914 epitomised not only the confidence investors had in the Lancashire cotton industry during this period, but also represented the ultimate development in factory construction. Inside the new mills, cast-iron columns now supported rolled steel girders on which was fixed concrete floors and then maple wood flooring. Side walls now free of structural loading had become huge expanses of window area, simply curtain walls, improving interior lighting from natural daylight and thus to some extent allowing greater width dimensions which increased spindle capacity. Externally, the prominent features of these flat-roofed blocks were their water towers displaying aloft the names of the mill companies. Numbers became concentrated in the Oldham and Bolton areas, whilst here and there, generally on the edge of a cotton town where land would be relatively cheap and readily available, the odd one or two appeared.

Near to Preston, Blackburn had Imperial Mill; Chorley, Talbot Mill; Coppull, Mavis & Coppull Ring; and Wigan, Trencherfield Mill. Preston's contribution would be Cliff and Tulketh Mills followed by one in nearby Bamber Bridge.

Compared to Tulketh Mill, the 1904 four-storey mill plus cellar of the Cliff Mill Spinning Company Ltd in Dundonald Street off New Hall Lane was much less attractive architecturally, even though it did have some artistic merit in the terracotta Doric style pillars on the top storey. The upper section of the water tower at the north-western corner of the block also presented some embellishment in classical style motifs and corners articulated with square Ionic pilasters. The engine house, adjacent to its four-bay boiler house at the south-eastern corner of the mill and near the freestanding circular chimney, was a much plainer building compared to Tulketh's.

Regarding the identity of the Cliff engine, one source of information, although anecdotal, mentioned a Yates & Thom

'The Golden Autumn': 1900 to The Great War

73. Cole, Marchent & Morley 'marine type' inverted vertical triple-expansion engine (three in-line cylinders with flywheel at one end) at Arkwright Mill.

74. Demolition of the engine house, Arkwright Mill.

horizontal cross compound of 1,400 horsepower with 27″ and 55″ bores × 5′ stroke. Corliss values were fitted and steam pressure was 165 psi from Yates & Thom boilers which were to have new fronts in c. 1939. Further clarification of a cross compound type was to be seen in a plan of the ground floor for Cliff Mill, found among other drawings at Centenary Mill; the plan showed the layout of two engine beds in keeping with a cross compound installation. Also shown in outline was the flywheel running at 65 rpm to provide a twelve-rope drive to the ground floor; an eight-rope one to the first floor; an eight-rope one to the second floor; and a seven-rope drive to the third floor. Cliff Mill had a spindle capacity of approximately 100,000 spindles for fine yarns on Dobson & Barlow mules, and its engine also ran by ropes a D. C. generator for lighting.

Reference DDX 1308/3 in the Lancashire Record Office is an account of the 14th Annual Ordinary General Meeting of Shareholders of the Cliff Spinning Company Ltd, which was to be held in St Mary's School, New Hall Lane, on Monday 20 January 1919, at 7.15pm. The balance sheet for 30 November 1918 shows the land valued at just over £3,389, and mill buildings,

75 (*opposite, top*). Cliff Mill from the air.

76 (*opposite, bottom*). Demolition of Cliff Mill, showing the cast-iron column, steel beam and concrete floor construction, typical of an early 1900s textile factory.

77. A plan showing the engine drive layout to the ground floor of Cliff Mill.

reservoir, engines, boilers, machinery, utensils etc., as per last account, were worth a little over £70,188. Additions during the year came to just over £250, and depreciation for the year came to £4,000. Nominal capital was made up of 100,000 shares at £1 each, whilst subscribed capital amounted to £50,000 which consisted of 100,000 shares of £1 each from which ten shillings per share had been paid out.

Mrs Mary Margerison, Mayoress of Preston, laid the foundation stone of Tulketh Mill in Balcarres Road on 13 May 1905. The mill, which was to be built by the local firm of Thomas Croft, was in production a week before its official opening ceremony on Wednesday, 11 July 1906. At this ceremony was again the Mayoress of Preston, on this occasion Mrs Ormerod, who officially named and started the engines which were in the form of a horizontal cross compound made by the Bolton firm of J. & E. Wood. Fitted with Corliss valves and Wood's trip gear, the 2,000 horsepower engine had 29″ and 58″ bores × 5′ stroke. Superheated steam entered the high pressure engine named 'Ashton' at about 150 psi pressure and a temperature of 430°F before exhausting at 40psi pressure to enter the low pressure engine, 'Preston'.

The engines could achieve a combined horsepower of 2,400 on overload, and each one was fitted with an air pump operated by a triangular plate lever on a front extending piston rod. Both pumps removed 1,750 gallons of condensate per minute at a

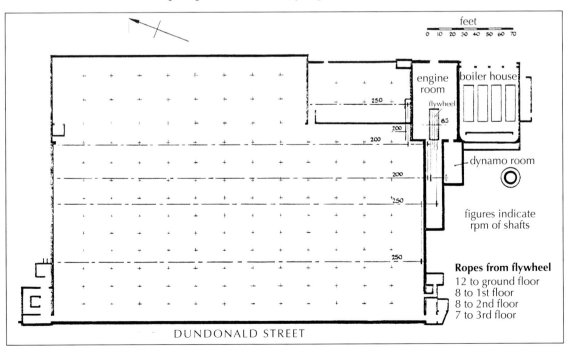

feet
0 10 20 30 40 50 60 70

engine room
boiler house
flywheel
250
200
65
200

dynamo room
200

250

figures indicate rpm of shafts

250

Ropes from flywheel
12 to ground floor
8 to 1st floor
8 to 2nd floor
7 to 3rd floor

DUNDONALD STREET

temperature of 112 degrees Fahrenheit from the condenser to the hot lodge; the two lodges at Tulketh having a total capacity of 1,750,000 gallons and a water depth of ten feet. Grooved for 44 ropes of 1¾″ diameter, the engine's 24′ diameter flywheel rotated at 66½rpm, and the ropes to the top floor drive pulley were 212′ in length.

Initially four Lancashire boilers were installed, each capable of raising 10,000 lbs of steam per hour, but in c. 1918, when the mill block underwent extension, a fifth boiler – a single flue Yorkshire type – was added to the bank of four, the arrangement being that one boiler was always on standby. Coal consumption varied in accordance with climatic conditions, the feed being 110 tons per week for the winter months and 75 tons per week during the summer; the engine operating on a vacuum of 12½ psi pressure below that of the atmosphere.

W. L. Holland, a Preston brass founder, was the first chairman, and the architect was Frederick William Dixon (1854–1935) of Trevelyan Buildings, Manchester, who had established his own practice in c. 1890. Between 1891 and 1914 Dixon was to design twenty two mills in Oldham alone, and the design of the water

78. The Tulketh Mill block of 1906 with an extension on the northern end (to the left of the photograph) of 1918. Behind, land had been set aside for a second mill scheme which never materialised. Its chimney is fitted with an anti-back draught device.

79. The fine proportions of the Tulketh Mill engine house alongside its boiler house.

towers on his mills were most individualistic, the Tulketh one being no exception. Even today, almost a century on, it has a modern look about it. Another architectural feature of Dixon's Mills would be the pronounced brick piers extending between each window to roof parapet level as at Tulketh where one pier is wider than the rest where the new extension began.

Originally the mill's freestanding circular chimney stood at just under 77 yards and was fitted with an anti-backdraught cap, common in Oldham at one particular period. This device was still in position at Tulketh in 1925 when the top part of the chimney was shrouded in scaffolding, but the cap was never considered a success and was later removed, most probably when the chimney was lowered about ten yards in the 1930s due to cracks in the brickwork. Arising from this work, impressive feature work was carried out at the top which unfortunately went in the 1960s when a further reduction came about resulting in the heavily banded structure of today standing at 60 yards. A few years ago, a draught-reducing cap was fitted to serve a modern, general heating boiler plant.

Apparently it had been the intention for the Tulketh block to be the spinning side of a double mill scheme with weaving facilities, but such a plan never materialised. Instead the existing mill block was lengthened in 1918 to offer a spindleage capacity

of 127,400 mule spindles and 12,600 on ring spinning machines for American and Egyptian yarn. The new extension had to be supported on pillars over a reservoir at the north end, and presented Tulketh with a top floor line shaft of 427 feet in length within which were incorporated six expansion joints, each with a gap of ⅜''. This shaft was reduced in diameter in stages beginning at 3½'' at the engine end to 1½'' by the time it had reached the extension part. It is said that only when the engine end had made two and a half revolutions did the far end of the shaft begin to rotate.

The engine chosen for the 1907 mill of the Bamber Bridge Spinning & Weaving Co. Ltd was also a J. & E. Wood example, but on this occasion it was a horizontal four cylinder triple expansion type. Little information has been found in connection with this superb engine which had a flywheel of 26' diameter to

81. The architect of Tulketh Mill was Frederick William Dixon of Manchester, who was well known for his individualistic water towers, the one at Tulketh being no exception.

provide drive for 127,500 mule spindles and a dynamo which supplied electricity for in excess of 900 lamps.

The firm of John & Edward Wood of Victoria Foundry, Bolton, was formerly known as Knight & Wood which had been established in 1838. By 1890, J. & E. Wood were building various types of mill engines and engaged in the making of steam engines for generating electric lighting. Their mill engines were to have outlet and inlet valves at the bottom of the cylinders, apparently for good economy, and another design characteristic of their engines was the starting valve table supported on Grecian-style fluted columns as at Tulketh. By 1914 the firm had closed after many a memorable engine installation. Phoenix Mill in Kirkham had a horizontal cross compound example of 600 horsepower to be named 'Commerce' and 'Industry'. The Bolton engine firm was represented at Cuerden Green Mills, near Lostock Hall by a horizontal cross compound made in 1905, whose starting valve table was directly in front of one cylinder seemingly on account of the rope drive running back over the engine room floor. Nearby, the Tardy Gate Manufacturing Co. Ltd Mill of 1908 also had a J. & E. Wood engine, whilst southwards at Chorley, Coppull and Wigan, impressive four cylinder triples of the Bolton firm appeared. Talbot Mill, Chorley had two in a double engine house, one driving the weaving shed, the other, the mill. Two also appeared in Coppull, one at Mavis Mill and the other at Coppull Ring, whilst in Wigan at Trencherfield Mill of 1907, J. & E. Wood installed their largest example, now preserved and a tourist attraction.

Cotton Mills of Preston

82. The engine at A.S. Orr's School Lane Mill, Bamber Bridge. The make of this fine engine is unknown. Note the steam pipe arrangement entering the high-pressure cylinder seen on the left of the photograph.
(*Harris Museum, Preston*)

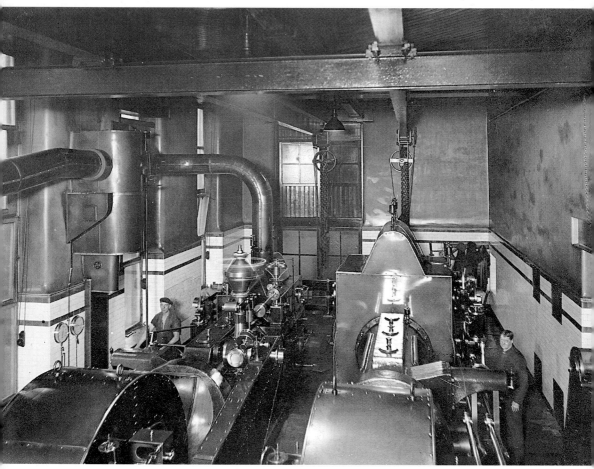

83. The rear of Bamber Bridge Spinning and Weaving Co. Ltd, showing the engine house projection.

Between 1904 and 1914, no fewer than seven new weaving establishments appeared on the Preston scene: Eldon Street Mill (1904); Progress (1906); Wharton (1907); Bute (c. 1910); Raglan (1912); Embroidery (1912); and Waverley Park (1914).

The engine for Eldon Street Mill, later known as Stocks Bridge, would be an 800 horsepower horizontal cross compound made in 1904 by Yates & Thom. Drive transmission was typical for a shed engine of the period; rope drive to a pulley on the first motion shaft and thence power transfer via bevel gearing to eighteen drive shafts in the shed. Cylinder bores were 18½" and 37" × 4′ 6" stroke, whilst condenser feed water and condensate cooling came from the canal some distance away near the mill's western boundary.

The architect for the new manufactory in December 1903, when it was referred to as the mill for the Eldon Street Mill Co. Ltd, was P. Pickup, architect and engineer of Mercantile Chambers, Burnley. In 1907, the manufactory is listed for James Lee & Brother, and in 1917, still under the same firm, is referred to as Stocks Bridge Mill. Like the rest of the new Preston manufactories built between 1904 and 1914, Eldon Street Mill was raised in the bright red machine brick of the period, its most attractive feature being its chimney which stood at the corner of Eldon Street and Parker Street, a structure representing a bricklayer's skill at his best. After a few feet its square base gave way to an octagonal form from which began the main circular stalk. Adjacent was the two-bay boiler house with its header tank, then the engine house from which ran the high panelled wall along Eldon Street, and behind it the gearing alley with the first motion shaft. Shed area was large especially after extensions had been carried out by 1912.

John & Adam Leigh Ltd in 1906 extended their weaving facilities with the building of Progress Mill in Shelley Road, next to their Brookhouse Mills. The engine chosen for Progress was a 500 horsepower horizontal cross compound made by Ashton, Frost Ltd of Bank Top Foundry, Blackburn. Cylinder bores were 16″ and 36″ on a 3′ stroke, the engine running at 84 rpm. Its steam raising plant would use the huge circular chimney which had been erected in 1872 in the adjacent mill yard.

Ashton, Frost were also to be represented at Wharton Mill, at the other side of Preston in Ribbleton. For this 1907 manufactory, the Blackburn firm would install a horizontal cross compound to be named 'Constance' after the mill owner's wife. This tiny engine had 12″ and 23½″ bores on a 2½′ stroke, and ran at 98 rpm to

84. The 1907 mill of the Bamber Bridge Spinning and Weaving Co. Ltd

'The Golden Autumn': 1900 to The Great War

produce 250 horsepower. In 1910, this manufactory was listed for Burrow's Ltd, and in 1922 whilst operating under the same firm was referred to as Emerson Road Mill. Initially the shed had 300 looms and around the time of the First World War another shed was added and a further 300 looms installed. Production was aimed at a variety of fabrics including poplin shirting, crepe-de-chine, voile corsetting, brocades, cloth for Africa, and umbrella coverings. Barrage balloon material was made there during the Second World War.

Bute Mill in Essex Street, off St Paul's Road, was a new addition to the list of cotton manufacturers for 1910 when it was represented by Taylor Bros. Its engine was to be a Yates & Thom compound, most likely a horizontal cross compound, which had 14″ and 27″ bores on a 3′ stroke. I still remember vividly the name of this manufactory displayed aloft on its circular chimney. J. & A. Leigh Ltd extended their weaving facilities yet again with the building of Raglan Mill in Raglan Street in 1912, a short distance from the firm's Brookhouse Mills. No details of its engine have been unearthed except for the mention of a horizontal cross

85. The engine house at Bamber Bridge Spinning and Weaving Co. Ltd. On the extreme right can be seen the dynamo room.

88 (*above*). Mills in the Shelley Road area, looking northwards. Bottom centre is Progress Mill of J. & A. Leigh Ltd, whose Brookhouse Mills are on the right. Left, alongside Shelley Road, is Shelley Road Mill, its weaving shed next to Parker Street Mill, to the north of which is Stocks Bridge Mill, then Embroidery Mill and, finally, Tulketh Mill at the top.

86 (*opposite, top*). The engine house (extreme left) of Stocks Bridge Mill, adjacent to the boiler house at the corner of Eldon Street and Parker Street.

87 (*opposite, bottom*). Demolition of Stocks Bridge Mill exposes the wall (extreme right) of the gearing alley which once contained the first motion shaft drive from the engine house seen at top centre.

compound. An aerial photograph shows the manufactory, its shed area lying in a north-south alignment alongside Raglan Street, whilst on a triangular area backing onto the main West Coast railway line is the lodge and what seems to be engine house and boiler house near the circular chimney in the north-east corner overlooking Bold Street Mill.

Embroidery Mill, just to the north of Eldon Street Mill, appeared under Cotton Manufacturers in the 1913 Directory for Birtwistle & Lawrence Ltd. Although there was a casual mention during research of the engine at Embroidery possibly being a Yates & Thom example, the finding of a drawing at the mill in 1978, then Dorman Smith Switchgear Ltd, led me to conclude that the engine was more than likely from the Blackburn works of Ashton, Frost & Co. Ltd. The drawing with an Ashton, Frost stamp on it showed elevation and plan of Embroidery, the engine beds clearly representative of a proposed horizontal cross compound installation which would be attended by one Lancashire boiler. Once again, the general layout of gearing alley and line shaft centres indicated a typical shed drive of the period, that is, rope drive from engine flywheel to a pulley on the first motion shaft

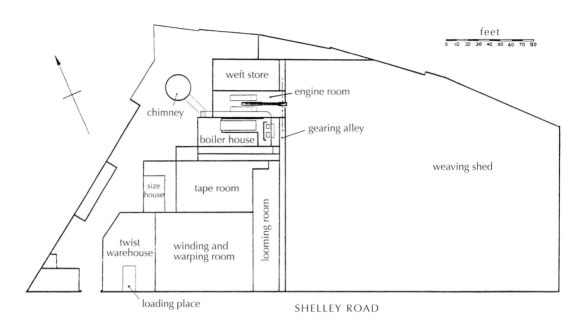

weft store

engine room

chimney

gearing alley

boiler house

size house

tape room

weaving shed

looming room

twist warehouse

winding and warping room

loading place

SHELLEY ROAD

feet

0 10 20 30 40 50 60 70 80

91 (*above*). Musgrave uniflow engine, made in 1913 for Progress Mill, Kirkham.

89 (*opposite, top*). This layout of J. and A. Leigh's Progress Mill of 1906 was typical of a manufactory (weaving) laid out on horizontal lines, i.e. on ground level.

90 (*opposite, bottom*). J. and E. Wood cross-compound engine of 1905 at the Cuerden Green Mills of Thom. Moss & Sons Ltd.

and thence into the shed by overhead line shafts from which belt drive to the looms would be taken, as at the nearby Progress Mill of J. & A. Leigh Ltd.

Ashton, Frost of Bank Top Foundry, Blackburn, were well known for their fine shed engines. The firm made very few spinning mill engines, probably their largest being the 1,500 horsepower horizontal cross compound of 1902 for the May Mill at Pemberton, Wigan. During the First World War the firm was engaged on munitions, manufacturing machine tools for making guns and projectiles, and also carried out large contracts on torpedo work. After the war the works reverted to its peacetime activities of making steam engines but due to financial difficulties closed in 1926. The second-hand engine at Crampoaks Mill, Longridge, was an Ashton, Frost single tandem made in c. 1906, and which had been installed by Clayton & Goodfellow of Blackburn in 1936.

Waverley Park Mill of 1914 was the last cotton manufactory to be built in Preston, and most probably why it did not appear in the 1917 Directory was because its opening was delayed due to the war. However, it was represented in the 1922 Directory

by Samuel Slater & Son who also worked Tennyson Road Mill opposite.

The Waverley Park engine was a uniflow of about 400 horsepower with a cylinder bore of 26″ diameter × 3′ stroke. Built by Musgraves of Bolton in 1914, it was to be named 'Rachel' after the mill owner's wife, and was connected directly to the first motion shaft. This was a common arrangement due to the high revolutions of this type of engine within which the whole expansion from boiler pressure to condenser vacuum occurred in a single cylinder.

The history of the uniflow's development is long and painfully slow. Jacques de Montgolfier sketched such an engine in 1825, and Jacob Perkins patented an engine based on the uniflow principle in 1827; yet the uniflow did not receive popularity until the second decade of the 1900s.

In 1885, a patent for such an engine had been taken out by Todd but this did not arouse a great deal of interest, which is surprising when one considers that during the 1880s there was a demand for high speed engines for electric lighting generators. So the idea of the uniflow would lie dormant until 1908 when a suitable valve gear for the engine would be designed and patented by Dr Johann Stumpf of Charlottenburg, and once initial teething troubles had been overcome, it was soon adopted for mill drive.

For the steam inlet, drop valves were used to give high steam economy, whilst for dealing with exhaust steam a number of circular openings were at the centre of the cylinder to be uncovered by the movement of the piston. Thus the inlet valves were never cooled by the exhaust steam, a design feature which supported the economic usage of steam.

There were many advantages in operating a uniflow, or unaflow as it was sometimes referred to, in comparison to a conventional engine. For example comparing a cross compound type with a uniflow of similar size reveals that a cross compound would have one more cylinder; six more valves; twenty-eight more rods/levers in its valve gear; twenty-four more brass bushed valve gear pins; and one more crank pin.

These extra components of the cross compound which absorbed

94. Layout of Embroidery Mill.

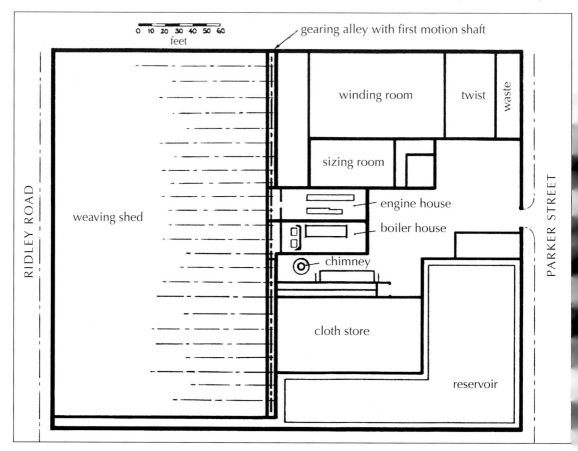

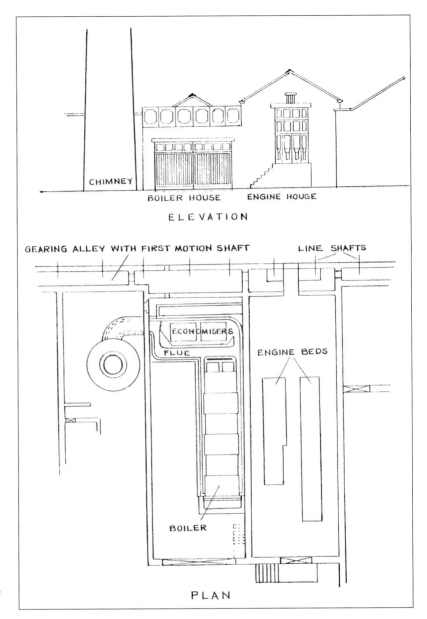

CHIMNEY

BOILER HOUSE   ENGINE HOUSE

ELEVATION

GEARING ALLEY WITH FIRST MOTION SHAFT   LINE SHAFTS

ECONOMISERS

FLUE   ENGINE BEDS

BOILER

PLAN

95. Elevation and plan of the power plant area at Embroidery Mill.

a great deal of frictional energy meant that the mechanical efficiency of the uniflow was much greater, as high as 94 per cent compared to about 91 per cent in a high-class cross compound. In addition, the simplicity of the uniflow could reduce breakdown liability and repair costs, and coupling the flywheel directly to the first motion shaft did away with the usage of ropes, their wear and possible breakage. Furthermore, lower costs could be met for lubrication oil, insurance and so on when operating a uniflow instead of a conventional type of engine.

Musgraves took out a licence in 1909 to build uniflow engines,

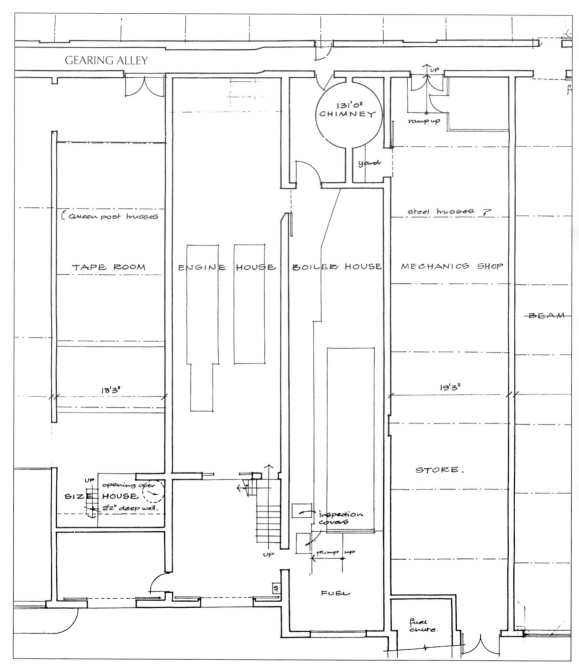

GEARING ALLEY

131'0"
CHIMNEY

ramp up

yard

Queen post trusses

steel trusses

TAPE ROOM

ENGINE HOUSE

BOILER HOUSE

MECHANICS SHOP

BEAM

18'3"

19'3"

STORE.

UP
SIZE HOUSE

opening over
2'2" deep well.

inspection
covers

ramp up

UP

FUEL

fuel
chute.

making one in 1913 and installing it in Progress Mill, Kirkham the following year. It had a 26½″ diameter bore × 2′ stroke, and at 130 rpm was rated at 400 horsepower. In 1929, Galloways of Manchester fitted a tailrod and slide, and a lightweight piston, and in this form the engine was more or less identical to the Waverley Park one in Preston.

A visit to Waverley Park Mill on 31 July 1978 found the engine

96. Engine House area at Emerson Road Mill of 1907. The gearing alley for the first motion staft is seen at the top of the drawing, while the extension to the left hand engine foundation bed would be to accommodate the condenser.

164

97. This photograph of 1965 shows what is supposedly the Ashton, Frost cross-compound at Emerson Road Mill, although the name on the low-pressure cylinder, seen on the left in tandem with the condenser, is not 'Constance' as one record disclosed. Were new cylinders fitted for extra power when a new shed was added around the time of the Great War?

house stripped of its upper floor and a boiler installed. Still in situ were the part-remains of the flywheel casing, whilst in the adjacent boiler house were two boilers, one having been adapted for hopper feed, the other for oil firing.

One of the last engines scheduled for a Preston mill prior to the outbreak of the First World War was a uniflow by Hick, Hargreaves of Bolton, seemingly arranged to be delivered at Easter, 1914, to the Peel Mill of J. R. & A. Smith. Several additions had been made to the mill in 1907 when two weaving sheds, a water tower for a sprinkler system, and supplementary buildings were built. However, letters of 1913 between Hick, Hargreaves and the proprietors of Peel Mill in connection with the new uniflow came to light in 1978 at J. R. & A. Smith's other Preston textile establishment, Manchester Mill. These correspondences were most kindly made available for inspection and proved interesting reading.

Initially a Musgrave uniflow engine had also been under consideration, evident from a comparison list of both makes of engine found amongst the letters. However, Hick, Hargreaves were to forward a letter containing 'intended sizes' of the new engine which was described as a 'Horizontal Central Exhaust Jet Condensing Engine', reference number E1713. The particulars were as follows:

Cylinder, 25″ diameter × 3′ 3″ stroke

Piston rod diameter, 5½″

RPM, 118

98. Waverley Park Mill of 1914 was the last cotton manufactory (weaving mill) to be built in Preston.

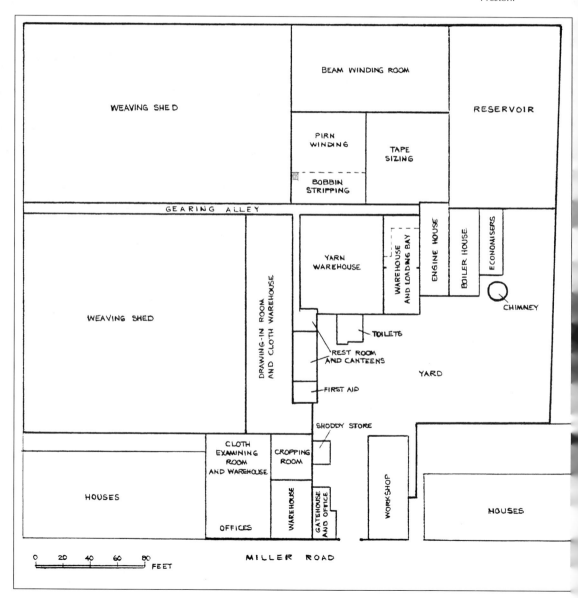

99. 'Rachel', the uniflow engine built by Musgraves of Bolton in 1914, for Waverley Park Mill. Due to the high revolutions of an engine of this type, its drive was connected directly to the first motion shaft via the flywheel whose casing can be seen in the corner. This photograph was taken in 1958.

Indicated horsepower, 510

Boiler pressure, 160 psi

Plain flywheel, 13' 0" diameter, in halves with a 17" face

Air pump, Edwards Twin Pumps each of 15" dia. × 12" stroke.

Stop valve, Hopkinson-Ferranti, 8" diameter.

Note the 'plain flywheel' which would not be grooved for rope drive but would be directly connected onto the first motion shaft due to the high revolutions of the engine.

A letter dated 21 November 1913 gave an estimate of steam consumption for the new engine which on full load would use 11 lbs (weight) per 1hp (indicated horsepower) hour of the superheated steam. In the offer of guarantee of steam consumption, Hick, Hargreaves promised to pay the purchasers a penalty at the rate of £100 for every pound (weight) of steam in excess, and should it be less, then the purchasers would pay a premium at the same rate.

On 2 December 1913 Hick, Hargreaves wrote to confirm the order for the engine, which with extras would cost £2,897. Delivery would be at Easter 1914, installation being completed after a stoppage of five weeks with the understanding that engine foundations would be put in as speedily as possible. Hick, Hargreaves also offered 50s. per ton for the old beam engine which they would take out.

J. R. & A. Smith Ltd were to stress to Hick, Hargreaves that they would pay a third of the cost for the engine on its delivery; the next third after it had been working satisfactorily on full load for two weeks; and the balance three months after the second payment.

Further modernisation was undertaken at Peel Mill in 1920 with the building of a circular chimney, mentioned earlier in chapter five, which must have been the last one erected for a textile mill in Preston. Its demolition came about in 1964, and an account in the *Lancashire Evening Post* of Friday 4 December tells of bricks being chipped out of its base to be replaced by piles of wood draped with paraffin-soaked rags to be set on fire. The account stated: 'As the chimney fell spot on in position, demolition foreman Matt Walker said, "She gave us no trouble".'

Hick, Hargreaves & Co. Ltd of Soho Foundry, Bolton, had

100. 'Rachel' at Waverley Park Mill.

'The Golden Autumn':
1900 to The Great War

been started by Benjamin Hick in 1833. In 1842 Hick died, the business passing to his son John, who in 1845 took into partnership William Hargreaves, the firm changing its name to Hick, Hargreaves & Company to supply locomotives, marine engines, and beam engines, and in 1864 was to introduce Corliss Valve Gear on its engines. In 1881, the firm supplied a 4,000 horsepower cross compound engine, and in 1891 built its first four cylinder triple. Meeting the advancement of the electrical power industry, Hick, Hargreaves installed engines in many of the early power stations, Deptford being one, which had been erected by the London Electric Supply Corporation under the direction of Ferranti in 1888.

When the Bolton-based engine firms of J. & E. Wood and John Musgraves & Sons Ltd, and the Manchester firm of Galloways Ltd closed, Hick, Hargreaves purchased their complete records, drawings and patterns, so maintaining an engine repair service.

In September 1978 I was given permission to inspect for Preston and district engine references, a huge collection of order books, cost books and drawings, formerly belonging to Hick, Hargreaves, which had been deposited in the basement of the High Street Branch Library, Bolton. At the time the collection had not been catalogued, which made reference-seeking difficult and time-consuming. However, the following came to light:

> Engine details for A. S. Orr Co. Ltd, Bamber Bridge – Order book, April 9th, 1919, for 1 new steel dashpot rod. Cost book, October 24th, 1919, for 2 brass bushes for dashpot rod end. Order book, September 28th, 1920, for 2 connecting rod cap bolts. Other references found were for W. Paley & Co., Preston – suction and delivery value seats; Wesham Mills, Kirkham – 5 thermometer pockets – very urgent; Selby Mill, Kirkham – steel clips for governor.

It is impossible to ascertain anywhere near the number of engine modifications and replacement power plant schemes undertaken in Preston and district mills between 1900 and 1914. So much engine data would be destroyed in the wake of mill closures years later, but the number must have been of some magnitude. The following, which have come to light during research, must therefore represent a small proportion of engine installations in Preston's mills during these years before the Great War besides those just mentioned.

In 1901, the local engine firm of J. Foster & Sons built what seems to have been a single cylinder vertical engine with a 21½" bore to work on 160 psi pressure for Eccles Bros's New Hall Lane Mill. In the same year, George Saxon of Spring Works, Openshaw, Manchester, made an inverted vertical triple of 400 ihp for the

Moor Brook Mill Co. Ltd, whilst for Aqueduct Street Mill a Musgrave single tandem compound of 1904 was installed as a shed engine to develop about 500 horsepower. The tandem had 19½″ and 35″ bores × 3′ stroke, and when another shed was built around 1914, the engine drove a generator to supply a 25 horsepower motor for winding, taping and preparation departments.

At Kay Street Mills, a 1905 built single tandem had 17½″ and 34″ bores × 3′ stroke, and the choice for number two mill of the Preston Cotton Spinning Company's Wellfield Mill was a 550–600 horsepower horizontal cross compound built by Musgraves in 1905. Working on 160 psi pressure it had 18″ and 38″ bores × 4′ stroke and ran at 68 rpm. For the number one mill, a 1,200 horsepower horizontal cross compound made by Yates & Thom in 1908 was fitted. Having 25″ and 52″ bores × 5′ stroke, it ran at 64 rpm on a working pressure of 145–160 psi.

Yates & Thom were represented at Shelley Road Mills by a horizontal cross compound made in 1908. Installed in a new engine house, it was rated at 950 horsepower with a mention of its flywheel being 19′ 6″ in diameter and grooved for 20 ropes of 2″ in diameter. A visit to the derelict engine house in January 1992, found oil staining where the flywheel bearings had been positioned at the end of a deep channel which ran to the far end of the engine house, passing between what had been the two cylinders, its depth extending from engine floor to ground level. I came to the conclusion that the channel had served as a rope race in a 'back driving' arrangement, similar to the one shown in the photograph of the Yard Works engine of 1915. Adjacent to, and on the other side of the eastern side wall of the engine house at Shelley Road Mill, was a covered rope race passage with a multi-grooved pulley in situ and aligned to what had been a weaving shed to the north.

George Saxon was to be represented again in Preston by a 500 ihp horizontal cross compound fitted with drop valves and built in 1910 for Alliance Works of E. B. Redmayne, where a new weaving shed had been erected in the same year. In 1919, Saxons remodelled the Victoria Engineering engine of 1885 at Vernon's number two mill, Penwortham.

The firm of George Saxon had been established in 1854 and was renowned for its large horizontal and vertical spinning mill engines, many of which were fitted into the new mills of the early 1900s, particularly in the Oldham districts. One particular type of engine associated with Saxons and never to appear on the Preston scene was the 'Manhattan', a compound engine having one cylinder in the vertical position, the other horizontal. Such

'The Golden Autumn': 1900 to The Great War

an arrangement of the cylinders achieved maximum power in a given space and the engine was used in the Manhattan, New York power stations in the early 1900s from whence came its name. Saxons made seven of these engines, one a double version installed in the Pear New Mill of 1912 in Bredbury, near Stockport. Its 76-rope flywheel was one of the widest in Lancashire. The intention was for the engine to drive two mills, the other to be the Apple which was never built, and in consequence only one side of the double Manhattan was used to drive the Pear.

The year 1906 saw the erection of an engine house next to the old one at Tennyson Road Mill, Preston, where in 1912 the building of a warehouse and another weaving shed would be undertaken. At Croft Street Mill, an engine house with rope race, executed in the red machine-made brick of the period, was to be yet another example of modernisation during those 'Indian summer' years of Preston cotton.

CHAPTER TEN

The Final Years

The period immediately following the Great War and up to just after the mid-1920s spanned the last years of mill engine building in Lancashire. For weaving shed drive the uniflow engine had established a reputation as an economic prime mover, and amongst the final batch of new engines for the Preston District mills alone, at least three would be uniflows. For the Nehesco Company Mill in Tarleton, Yates & Thom would provide a 250 horsepower example in *c.* 1920, whilst Clayton & Goodfellow would install one of 200 horsepower in 1922 at the Bee Mill, Ribchester. The third uniflow was another Yates & Thom engine, this time of 450 horsepower to be made in 1924 for the Croston Manufacturing Company Mill which had been established in 1887, a cross compound providing geared drive to a shed. In 1922, a new shed was built and the 1924 uniflow, named 'Edward Walmsley', installed to drive the shed and the old part. Fosters of Preston provided a new boiler to steam at 160 psi pressure, and the new engine which had a 27½″ bore × 2′ 6″ stroke ran at 140 rpm on superheated steam. As was usual in a shed uniflow installation, the flywheel of the Croston engine was fixed directly onto the first motion shaft.

A letter of 16 May 1918 from the Vulcan Boiler & General Insurance Company Limited, Manchester, to Paul Catterall & Son Ltd's New Hall Lane Mill in Rigby Street, Preston, stated that serious consideration should be given to the replacement of the engine power at the mill. Prior to this letter, the mill had been corresponding since at least 1899 with several engineering firms regarding problems in its engine plant, the single McNaughted beam with tandem compound pusher engine mentioned in chapter four. There had even been an attempt to sell the engines and boilers by auction which had been scheduled for Thursday 21 April 1887.

The letter of 16 May 1918 was one of several found at the mill soon after its closure in the early 1970s, each one being part of an interesting chain of correspondence which finally paved the way for a new engine, in situ in April 1920, in a new engine house.

The Final Years

In 1894, a new spur wheel had been fitted by Fosters, and in 1899 it was decided that the mill needed extra power to put on more ring spindles, the beam engine and its pusher requiring modification in order to cope with the increase in spindleage. From some of the letters of that year, it was apparent that the engines were in need of repair anyway. A letter dated 23 September 1899, from Joseph Foster & Sons of Soho Foundry, Preston, illustrated this situation, part of it reading:

Gentlemen,

Our price for the repairs to your Beam Engine, the work consisting of the following parts:

One Mild Steel Crank Shaft turned and planed, the neck next to the crank to be 15″ diar by 20 inches long, and swelled up for the flywheel to 16″ diar, boring out the two present eccentrics, taking crank off old shaft, and refixing same on new one with steel key would be £57.0.0. net (Fifty-seven pounds) net.

For one new crankshaft pedestal and cap ____

For a new Mild Steel Piston Rod ____

For one new Mild Steel Crosshead with necks, 5 inch diar machined

101. The uniflow engine of 1924 at the Croston Manufacturing Company Mill.

and fitted with new cotter, our price would be £22.10.0 net (Twenty-two pounds ten shillings) net.

For one new Mild Steel Beam centre neck 5 inch diar, ____

For a new cast iron cylinder cover _____

For two new McNaught Links fitted with best Gun-metal steps, 5 inch bored, cast iron blocks, gibs and cotters, machined and fit up here our price would be £68.0.0 net (sixty-eight pounds) net. in all cases the old materials to belong to us. The whole delivered at your mill but not fixed.

We shall be pleased to receive your order, which shall have our best attention.

We return the Vucan Boiler Insurance Company's letter of August 3rd. In any case the cotter in the high pressure cross-head should be replaced as quickly as possible, as it is very weak. We agree with the Insurance Co.'s suggestions.
 We are, Yours faithfully,
  Jos. Foster & Sons,
   A.F.

Clearly the engines needed a major repair and a short time later a letter dated 20 October 1899, from Yates & Thom arrived and read:

Dear Sirs,

 In response to your request of the 27th. ult, our Mr Watson visited your mill on the 30th and made an examination of the engine in view of your proposal to increase the load by 50H.P. The result of his examination was placed before our Mr Thom who also called on you on the 11th. inst. and we have now given the question our careful consideration.

 We find the beam engine is more heavily loaded than the Horizontal Engine and by replacing the High Pressure Horizontal cylinder with a new one, about 2 inches larger in diameter, you would obtain the 50 I.H.P. required without putting any additional work on the beam engine.

 We recommend you therefore to have this done. It would require new cylinder piston, piston rod, valve spindle, eccentric & rod, and probably a new throttle valve and pipe for the main steam range to the new cylinder. We should also advise a new girder to replace the broken one extending from the front end of the slides to the crank shaft pedestal.

 We have carefully considered the question of putting Corliss valves to the new cylinder but scarcely think the job would be worth the extra cost involved in doing so.

We have not yet had time to get out an estimate of the cost of this work but will endeavour to have it ready for Tuesday when our representative may see you on Change in Manchester.

Meanwhile,

We remain, Yours Obediently,

Yates & Thom.

A letter dated four days later, from the Blackburn engine builders read:

Dear Sirs,

Further to ours of the 20th inst., we have now gone carefully into the cost of making the proposed alterations to your horizontal Engine to enable you to obtain more power and have pleasure in offering to supply the following.

One new high pressure cylinder 18″ diameter and 7′ 0″ stroke … We do not advise Corliss Cylinder Valves. The extra cost would not give an adequate return for the outlay, and the working parts of both engines are light.

The letter continued to mention parts that would need replacing and at the end there was a postscript which strongly recommended the replacement of the crosshead of the McNaught cylinder on the beam engine as it was very weak.

The next piece of information about the beam engine and its pusher was on two sheets of paper giving particulars of tests carried out on both engines on 28 October 1902 by R. Davies & Son, Consulting Engineers, Blackburn. Most of this information is as follows, and indicator diagrams were also drawn on the papers.

Horizontal Engine

High Pressure Cylinder 16¼ inch diameter, stroke 7 feet, indicated horsepower 83.51, RPM = 29.

Front. Average pressure 33.5 lbs, maximum pressure above atmosphere 64 lbs.

Back. Average pressure 32 lbs, maximum pressure above atmosphere 58.5 lbs.

Low Pressure Cylinder 30¼ inch diameter, 7 feet stroke, indicated horsepower 90.61, RPM = 29.

Front. Average pressure 10.5 lbs, maximum vacuum 10.5 lbs, maximum pressure above atmosphere 13.5 lbs.

Back. Average pressure 10 lbs, maximum vacuum 11 lbs, maximum pressure above atmosphere 8.5 lbs.

Boiler pressure 75 lbs, temperature of ejection water 116 degrees Fr., temperature of injection water 90 degrees Fr.

Beam Engine

High Pressure Cylinder 36 inch diameter, stroke 3ft. 6in., indicated horsepower 215.97, RPM = 29.

Low Pressure Cylinder 41⅜ inch diameter, stroke 7 feet., indicated horsepower 194.34, RPM = 29.

Boiler pressure 75 lbs.

High Pressure

Top Average pressure 34 lbs.

Maximum pressure above atmosphere 68 lbs.

Bottom Average pressure 35 lbs.

Maximum pressure above atmosphere 69 lbs.

Low Pressure

Top Average pressure 12 lbs, maximum vacuum 10.5 lbs,

Maximum pressure above atmosphere 9.5 lbs.

Bottom Average pressure 11.5 lbs, maximum vacuum 10.5 lbs,

Maximum pressure above atmosphere 8.5 lbs.

Temperature of ejection water 124 degrees Fr.

Temperature of injection water 90 degrees Fr.

These particulars with the addition of indicator diagrams must have arrived with, or around the time of a letter, dated 6 November 1902 from Robert Davies & Son, part of which read:

Dear Sirs,
We Indicated, Examined and took the necessary particulars of Engines at New Hall Lane Mills, Preston on the 28th and the 30th of October and the 3rd November with the view of Increasing the Indicated Horse Power ...
The enclosed Diagrams show the present Indicated Horse power to be 584. The valves are in fair Adjustment ... the Boiler Pressure is Not made available on the High Pressure Pistons. There is a loss of 7½ lbs on the Beam Engine and 13½ lbs in the Horizontal Engine. Also the vacuum in both Engines is defective. Only 10½ lbs in Beam

Engine and 10¾ lbs in the Horizontal Engine. This defect causes a loss of 35 Indicated Horse Power and is caused by your Injection Water being of too High a Temperature.

The letter also mentioned that for the proposed 2,700 ring spindles with preparation machinery, 60 indicated horsepower would be required and any increase in power would require new engine parts, and ended:

> To Fix a New Engine in the Mill Yard adjoining the present Engine House say to develop 150 Horse Power, to take the Increase of Power and reduce the Power on the present Engines would be more economical in Fuel, but more costly.
> Hoping this Report will be satisfactory ...

Nothing seems to have been done to solve the ageing power plant problem until some years later, towards the end of 1911 when on 20 December Yates & Thom wrote out an estimate for three new Lancashire boilers suitable for 160 psi pressure; a correspondence of 10 January 1912 confirmed receipt of the order. As to the engine at the mill, it would be 1918 when Paul Catterall & Son arranged for a special service examination to be undertaken on a second-hand engine with the objective of installing it in their Preston Mill.

The engine, a horizontal compound Corliss valve, side by side example, had been made by Carmichael & Co. Ltd, of Ward Foundry, Dundee in 1905 and had been standing since about 1913 at the Guardbridge Paper Co. Ltd Mill, Guardbridge, Fife. The report following the examination stated that the engine would require a complete overhaul; the extract dated 29 April 1918.

Soon afterwards, a letter of 16 May from the Vulcan Boiler & General Insurance Company Limited, Manchester, was to present a radical solution to the engine problem at the Preston Mill, stating that serious consideration should be given to the replacement of the engine power. Four different types of drive were presented for consideration:

> Scheme 1. Driving by means of a high class steam engine and transmitting the power to the various sections by ropes.
> Scheme 2. Driving by means of a steam geared turbine and transmitting the power to the various sections by ropes as in No. 1 scheme.
> Scheme 3. Generation of electrical current by means of a turbo alternator and driving each section by electric motors.
> Scheme 4. Purchase of electric current from a public supply and installing electric motors for driving the various machines.

The letter continued:

We have given careful consideration to the whole of the above methods and taking as long a view as is possible of the developments in power production and transmission, we consider that you would be quite safe in adopting the No. 1 Scheme. This scheme as you know is one that has proved itself to be economical in the use of coal and reliable in operation.

With regard to Scheme 2, at the present time geared turbines are being developed and it is probable in a few years time that they will be in more general use ...

Scheme No. 3. This scheme would be quite in order, but the high initial cost would be prohibitive and the coal used under such a scheme would be a little greater than in either No. 1 or No. 2 scheme. The advantage of this scheme would consist in the almost absolute steadiness of drive on the spindles ...

Scheme No. 4. This scheme has generally the same qualities as No. 3 scheme ... The cost of the electrical equipment, that is motors, cables, starting switches etc., would be about 50% of the total cost of No. 1 Scheme.

Later on in the letter the following comment was made:

Probably in the course of a few years' time there will be a public supply of current in your district at a fairly low price, but we do not think that such a supply of current will compete successfully with a high class steam engine such as mentioned in No. 1 Scheme ... It should also be remembered that even if current were purchased you would still require steam for heating the Mill, and such steam could not be generated at the same high efficiency as steam which is generated in bulk in large Lancashire boilers ...

After suggesting that No. 1 Scheme would be the best, the letter continued:

The best arrangement of engine appears to be to place a tandem engine in the room near to the chimney in accordance with the drawing which Mr Scholes saw when he was at the Mill. Extreme care will however, require to be taken with the foundation for the outer bearing of the crankshaft. This foundation is very close to the chimney and there is an existing flue at this point which does not tend to improve matters ...

Regarding the type or make of engine we consider you should obtain as high a class of engine as is possible. A few thousand pounds saved on the cost of the whole scheme due to putting in a second hand engine would, we think, in the long run prove unsatisfactory ...

... Probably by placing the order now you will obtain earlier delivery of the engine after the War, and you would, therefore, sooner be able to operate the full complement of spindles.

102. Copy of a drawing found at Paul Catterall & Son's New Hall Lane Mill in Maitland Street.

The Final Years

No further letters were found at the mill to establish what Paul Catterall & Son Ltd did next regarding the acquisition of a new engine, only a drawing, dated 19 April 1920, which had the title: 'Plan of Driving from the new engine which was installed at Paul Catterall Ltd., Preston', the word 'was' indicating that the engine was already in situ by that date. This drawing, which is reproduced in this chapter, shows what appears to be a single tandem compound and its most interesting array of ropes driving to the various sections of the mill. Its make has never been established,

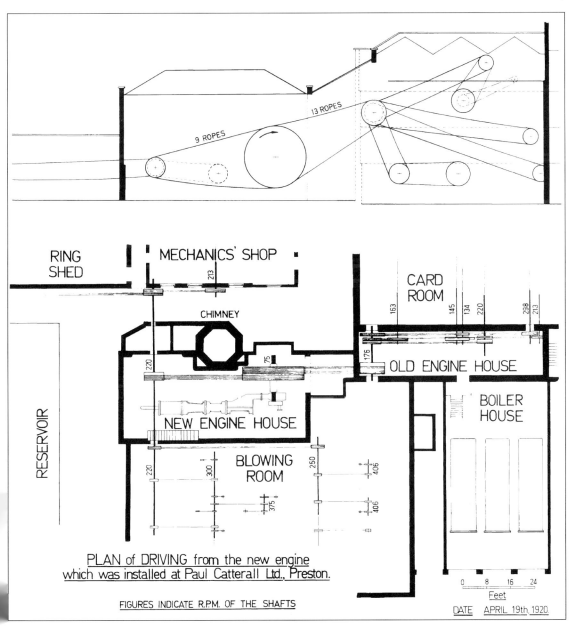

PLAN of DRIVING from the new engine which was installed at Paul Catterall Ltd., Preston.

FIGURES INDICATE R.P.M. OF THE SHAFTS

DATE   APRIL 19th, 1920.

but considering the past correspondence with Yates & Thom, the engine was quite possibly a product of their Canal Foundry in Blackburn. A visit there in 1973 to search for details of the engine proved fruitless, pre-1940 references having been thrown away and most of the engine drawings burnt during 'tidying up' operations.

Probably the last engine to be installed in a Preston Mill was the Pollitt & Wigzell horizontal cross compound fitted in a new engine house of 1921 at Manchester Mill.

A specification from the Vulcan Boiler & General Insurance Co. Ltd, dated March 1920, gives the following particulars for the engine:

> Superheated steam at 160 lbs pressure and a temperature of 550°F, 520 IHP with maximum economy and to drive 650 IHP satisfactorily and economically. A vertical air pump and jet condenser at rear of L.P., designed to give a vacuum of 26″ with a barometric pressure of 30″ when condensing 7,500 lbs of steam and supplied with injection water at 65°F.

The engine was Pollitt & Wigzell's No. 901 and had 18″ and 36″ bores × 4′ stroke. Running at 81 rpm, the flywheel drove the first motion shaft by fourteen ropes of 1¾″ diameter which

104 (*opposite*). Removal of the floor in the new engine house of c.1920 at Paul Catterall & Son's New Hall Lane Mill at the corner of Rigby Street and Maitland Street. In the foreground is one of the mill's reservoirs.

103. Multi-grooved pulley for rope drive at Paul Catterall and Son's New Hall Lane Mill in Maitland Street.

105. Demolition scene in the
'new' engine house at
Catterall's New Hall Lane Mill.

were fitted in June 1921. The positioning of the condenser on the
engine room floor instead of underneath, was characteristic of
this firm of engine builders.

Pollitt & Wigzell of Bank Foundry, Sowerby Bridge, Yorkshire,
had been founded by Timothy Bates in 1786, the firm being largely
millwrights until 1834 when John Pollitt began engine building.
In 1865 he was joined by E. Wigzell. The firm's last steam engine
was built in 1923 and closure of the works came in 1931.

The new engine house of 1921 at Manchester Mill blended well
with the bright red brick frontage of the mill which had been
subjected to a rebuilding programme in the early 1900s, possibly
c. 1903 when a warehouse and weaving shed were built. Even
though the mill had its own reservoir, it apparently at one time
also used the condensing facilities of the nearby India Mill.

By the period 1910–13, the British cotton industry's share of
world trade had fallen to 58 per cent compared to the 82 per cent
it had in 1882–84. Production was still on a downward trend by
the end of the First World War due to further decline in its export
trade. Prior to the war, European competition in Near East markets
and Japanese competition in Far Eastern ones had been evident.
During the war Japan had become an efficient and low-wage

The Final Years

106. Pollitt & Wigzell engine at Manchester Mill, Preston. The engine condenser is on the bottom right of the photograph.

107. Rope drive of the same engine to the first motion shaft.

competitor for world markets, whilst India had partaken in a rapid mill-building programme. By 1912–13, India had taken 36 per cent of the British production of cotton piece goods, and by 1926–28 British exports were two thirds of their pre-war volume.

Of the 60 Preston mills operating in 1927, that is discounting those outside the town boundary such as Higher Walton Mills and Flats Mills, 21 were to have closed by 1936. Marsh Lane, Bushell Street, Fylde Road Shed, Frenchwood, Astley Field, Moor Park, Lutwidge, India, and Aqueduct Street Mills closed between 1927 and 1932. These were followed by Bloomfield, Albert, Caledonia, Bank Top (which would re-open), Springfield, Moor Hall, Alliance Works, New Hall Lane (opposite Centenary), Wellington, Victoria, Wellfield, and Ribbleton Mills, which went into closure between 1932 and 1936.

The years 1936 to 1938 saw British exports accounting for only 46 per cent of production, the home market becoming more important than the export trade, and the protected rayon section supplying about one sixth of the total consumption of cotton and rayon textiles.

Preston's contribution to the man-made fibre industry was the building of Courtauld's Red Scar Works at Ribbleton in the 1930s, which had all steam turbine installation attended by coal-fired boilers and two cooling tower condensing facilities. The power plant also provided extraction steam and was independent of any outside power source, even though some power could be taken from the National Grid if and when circumstances demanded such.

108. Engineer and assistants with the new Pollitt & Wigzell cross-compound engine at Manchester mill in c.1922. (*Harris Musem, Preston*)

109. Behind the remains of the chimney of 1864 at Manchester Mill can be seen the new engine house of 1921 for the Pollitt & Wigzell engine. Dominating the scene is the bright red machine brick frontage of the early 1900s rebuild, complete with water tower.

The introduction of the Grid in the 1920s brought about a network of power stations throughout the country. In Preston, the first half of the Ribble Generating Station No 1 at Penwortham was completed by the end of 1924, the other half being finished in 1928, its main generating and condensing plants having been made by English Electric Co. Ltd. Each of the four turbo-alternators had a continuous maximum rating of 15,000 kws and ran at 3,000 rpm to deliver three-phase current at 50 cycles, 6,600 volts. Eight Babcock & Wilcox boilers of the marine cross-drum type with a maximum evaporation rate of 80,000 lbs per hour each, provided steam conditions of 325 psi pressure at 700 degrees Fahrenheit, with water for condensing being drawn from the River Ribble.

So it was in an atmosphere of mill closures and the now-possible availability of grid current, that the remaining workforce of Preston's mill engines operated as the Second World War approached. Their final demise was now inevitable.

Conscription during the Second World War was one of the wartime measures to affect the British cotton industry whereby arose the need to release labour. Also to release storage space for the war effort, and to conserve shipping which reduced raw cotton supplies. Such measures were responsible for the closing down of about one third of the spinning and weaving capacity of the textile industry, and the resulting limited production was then required primarily for military and essential home services.

After the war, the British cotton industry, through its inability to recruit its depleted labour force, failed to recapture its own markets and those of its competitors, Japan and Europe, whose own cotton industries had been seriously affected by the war. At the end of the war, the British industry's labour force was 52 per cent of the 1937 level, with a heavy annual retirement and very small recruitment. By 1951 the industry's share of world cotton textile exports was 15 per cent, the decline being due mainly to the restriction on imports into India and Pakistan; Indian competition in the Colonies; and European competition in Scandinavia.

From 1953 a further decline came about because of Japanese competition in the Colonies and Dominions, and also European export competition. In 1954 and 1955 cotton cloth from India and Hong Kong began arriving in increasing quantities, and by the end of 1955 it had amounted to about 12 per cent of the United Kingdom production. Many British firms by this time had gone out of business or had been taken over after facing overwhelming costs of re-equipping. By 1955 about 1,000 operatives per week were leaving the industry, and during the year about 2,000,000 mule equivalent spindles were scrapped of which perhaps two thirds were in mills going out of business.

As to the Preston scene, the following mills had closed between 1936 and 1940; Deepdale, Steam, Moor Brook, Bold Street, and Parker Street. The sale of engines and boiler plant at Deepdale Mill was scheduled for Wednesday, 15 April 1936. Particulars from the Sale Catalogue, now in the safe keeping of the Lancashire Record Office under reference DDX1623, Deepdale Mill, 'Plans and Sale Catalogue 1888 – 1936,' lists a horizontal tandem engine with 15″ and 28″ bores × 3′ 6″ stroke having slide valves. The cast-iron flywheel 13′ diameter, was 13″ side on face and 17″ depth of rim; the helical toothed spur wheel being 9′ diameter and 10″ wide on face. A vertical condenser and air pumps are mentioned as well as the cast-iron box frame engine bed which measured 30′ 6″ in length.

There is no doubt whatsoever that this was the same engine working at the mill in the mid-1890s, the Classification of that particular period listing the same bores and stroke, and a power rating of 48 horsepower. As to its year of manufacture, then 1888

110. Celebration scene in the weaving shed at Hawkins' Greenbank Mill, c.1935. (*Harris Musem, Preston*)

as presented in the 'Plans and Sale Catalogue' heading, could well be the date when it arrived as a replacement to an ageing beam engine, the mill having been part of the Preston scene for some years at that date, having been erected by the beginning of the 1850s as mentioned in chapter four.

In 1851, Deepdale Mill, which was built near the corner of Deepdale Mill Street and Isherwood Street, was occupied by William Lancaster & Co., a firm which was still there in 1855 as manufacturers of muslin. Two years later a change in ownership had come about by way of Lancaster & Isherwood who were the representatives in 1860. In March 1862 the full complement of 600 looms were at work six days per week, but due to the pending Cotton Famine, the manufactory was expected to close when the stock of cotton on hand had been worked up. Deepdale Mill was working in 1865 under William Lancaster & Company, the same firm representing it in 1874. By 1877, Wood, Hampson & Company were in control, and in 1882, when the manufactory had 538 looms, Hampson, Smith & Company are running the business. Around this time, a further change in control would come about, Hampson & Fish being the representatives from 1882/83 to at least 1889. L. Heyworth & Son are in charge in 1892 and still listed in 1895, but by 1898, the manufactory was operating under the title of the Deepdale Mill Co. Ltd until closure in 1936.

Other particulars presented for the April sale of 1936, referred to one boiler, 8′ in diameter and 30′ in length, made by W. & J. Yates of Blackburn, which had last been insured for 100 lbs pressure. Also for sale was a Green's Fuel Economiser, and an inverted vertical compound steam engine named 'Gwynne', which was in the tape sizing room. High pressure cylinder was 6″ diameter, whilst the low pressure one was 9″ diameter × 9″ stroke. The engine, complete with balance wheel and belt pulley, had a 'Pickerings' governor, and the 3″ exhaust pipe passed through the roof.

Cotton Mills of Preston

111. Horrockses, Crewdson & Co.'s Yard Works and Sovereign Mill, Preston. The disused engine houses and the electrical switchgear show that in 1940, when this drawing was made, Yard Works was operating on electrical drive.

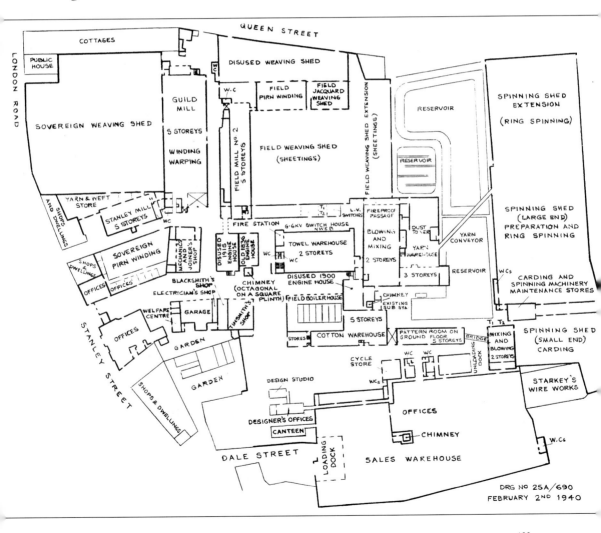

The Final Years

Although there would be no further mill closures between 1940 and 1944 in Preston, three more, Spa Mill, Grimshaw Street Mill, and Fylde Road Mill, had shut down as textile concerns by the time the 1948 Trade Directory was published, which listed what would be representative of Preston's remaining operative textile mills for the Guild Year of 1952. These mills were as follows: Emerson Road, Kent Street, Bank Top, Stocks Bridge, Brookfield, Peel, Manchester, Embroidery, Queen's, Bute, Ashton Shed, Alexandra, New Hall Lane (Rigby Street), Cliff, Tulketh, Tennyson Road, Waverley Park, Arkwright, Shelley Road, Greenbank, Park Lane, St Paul's Road, Hartford, Yard Works, New Preston, Centenary, Sovereign, Fishwick, Raglan Street, Brookhouse, and Progress; in all, 31 mills involving 19 firms.

In October 1948, the fourth turbo-alternator set and the last two boiler units had been put into service at the No. 2 power station at Penwortham, work having begun on this second electricity generating on the Penwortham site in August 1940. Because the River Ribble was unable to provide sufficient condenser circulating water at all times, that is including periods of low tide, for both stations, two underground tunnels, inlet and discharge respectively, were constructed between the new power station and the Albert Edward Dock on the opposite river bank. This meant that during periods of low tide, the cooling water capacity of the Dock could be utilised.

So by the beginnings of the 1950s, grid current had long been an attractive proposition for mill drive in Preston, some factories having already installed it such as Greenbank Mills, Queen's Mill, and Yard Works. Others, such as Brookhouse Mill and Shelley Road Mill, were embarking on this new power technology, whilst in a number of mills the steam engine still continued to provide motive power.

Kent Street Mill still had its beam engine; Brookhouse Mill its vertical compound; Shelley Road Mill its horizontal cross compound; and Fishwick Mill its vertical compound; but like the rest of Preston's remaining engines, their days were numbered. The engine at Embroidery Mill had gone some time between 1948 and 1950, and by the 1950s, four main electric motors had been fitted within the rope race at Centenary Mill, one to each floor. The ground floor which housed preparation and carding machinery, was powered by a 200 horsepower motor; the first floor for ring spinning by a 220 horsepower one; whilst the second and third floors for mule spinning were each run from a 350 horsepower motor. Scutching and mixing sections were attended by small unit motors.

Just before 1955, electric motors were being installed on each line shaft at Waverley Park Mill, and shortly afterwards its Musgrave uniflow was scrapped after much trouble with a bearing had been experienced.

A few miles away in Longridge, G. Whittle & Co. at their Stonebridge Mill in 1956 decided to shut down for scrap the mill's horizontal cross compound engine which had been made by Joseph Clayton & Co., Preston, in 1877, who also had provided the two boilers. The engine had 18″ and 32″ bores × 4′ 6″ stroke, and drove a 15′ diameter flywheel at 48 rpm, the drive being transmitted by rim gearing to a 6′ 6″ diameter pinion wheel on the shed shaft. Stonebridge Mill, often referred to as Whittle's Mill, had been erected in 1850, a single beam engine providing

The Final Years

112. Mule spinner at Horrockses Yard Works.

drive for a weaving shed. As business grew, a further shed was built in 1877, the Clayton cross compound arriving to drive both sheds. Years later, another shed would be built to be powered by the same engine, which had to develop more than its design rating of 350 horsepower. Right up to 1956, the Preston-built engine had run with little trouble, but the steam pressure on the original boilers had been reduced to 50 psi, and the installation of new boilers would have been too costly. So all was scrapped and the mill closed down.

Longridge at one time had three other mills: Queen's, built in 1874; Victoria, erected in 1862; and Crumpax, known as Crampoakes Mill in Berry Lane, built in 1851 for William Marsden and James Hayhurst. Both names are recorded in Yates's Book of Engine Lists 1857–76 as 'Messrs Hayhurst & Marsden, Longridge, 1868', for a single compound beam engine with 30⅛″ and 31⅛″ bores on respective strokes of 3′ and 6′, the high pressure cylinder having slide valves, and the low pressure one, Cornish valves. Also mentioned in the data was a governing valve, and it was whilst on a visit to Stocks Bridge Mill, Preston, in August 1972, that I was told a rather amusing story about the engine at Crampoakes Mill. It had been a beam engine, the original engine, which apparently for some reason did not have a governor, and at times, the engine would 'run away', shuttles flying out of looms which were running too fast, and weavers making a quick exit. Once, the engine during one of its 'mad moments' buckled shafting causing roof damage. The stop buttons did not work because batteries were flat, and the only way the engine could be controlled was by regulating the steam pressure. In 1936, Clayton & Goodfellow of Blackburn fitted an Ashton, Frost tandem engine which originally had been a ship's engine, made sometime between 1906 and 1909. This engine had rope drive, about ten ropes, and the mill also had a donkey engine, a single cylinder one of 15–20 horsepower which ran the tape room during the lunch hour. The mill closed in 1959.

In Preston, Stocks Bridge Mill closed in 1956, following which its Yates & Thom horizontal cross compound was scrapped, and when Vernon – Carus took over the manufactory in 1959, a diesel engine for generating electricity was installed in the engine room. At Manchester Mill, the Pollitt & Wigzell cross compound was stopped in July 1958, its demolition beginning on 20 September. During the following year, the 1894 Yates & Thom cross compound at Brookfield Mill was scrapped with the closure of the mill.

The replacement by motor drive of the Cole, Marchent & Morley vertical triple at Arkwright Mill took place in 1960, and on 4 June 1961, demolition of the Hick, Hargreaves uniflow at Peel Mill began. In January 1962 Horrockses, Crewdson & Co. Ltd announced that its twelve-acre Yard Works was to close in March, and six months later the firm closed its Cliff Mill in Dundonald Street with the loss of another 150 jobs. When Cliff closed its cross compound engine had been stopped before this date as the installation of electric drive had almost been completed when closure came. The mill was a victim of the uncertain and unstable economic climate of the early 1960s, and its closure, even after much modernisation had taken place, came suddenly and unexpected.

In 1965, the Ashton, Frost cross compound at Emerson Road Mill was broken up, and what must have been the final engine in Preston to yield to the demolition hammer was the J. & E. Wood cross compound at Tulketh Mill which went with the mill's closure in the second half of the 1960s. At the time of its breaking up, the engine was in excellent order, and it should undoubtedly have been preserved as a part of Preston's industrial heritage. When the mail order firm of the Peter Craig organisation arrived at Tulketh in May–June 1968, the engine had already gone, and on the mill floors, machinery which had recently been updated in design, was still in situ. Eventually the engine house would become a waste package room; a sad and unbecoming end.

Following pages: maps (1912) showing sites of cotton mills

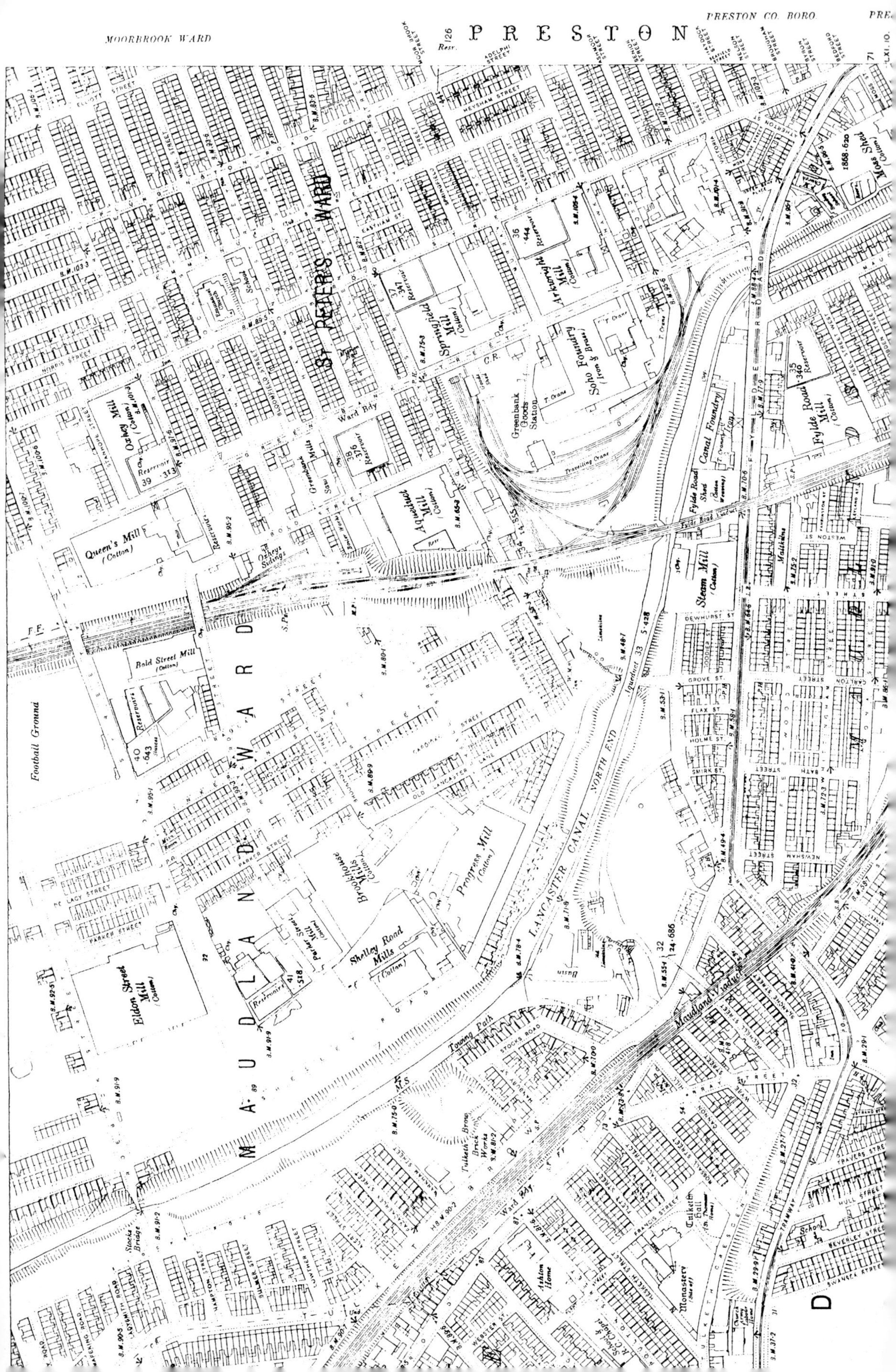

ST PETERS WARD

MAUDLAND WARD

ELLIOT STREET

HEYSHAM STREET

ADELPHI STREET

Oxley Mill (Cotton)

Greenbank Mills

Spring Mill (Cotton)

Aqueduct Mill (Cotton)

Arkwright Mill (Cotton)

Soho Foundry (Iron & Brass)

Canal Foundry

Fylde Road Mill (Cotton)

Moss Shed

Greenbank Goods Station

Ward Bdy.

Travelling Crane

Queen's Mill (Cotton)

Reservoirs

Oxheys Sidings

Bold Street Mill (Cotton)

Reservoirs

Football Ground

Steam Mill (Cotton)

Aqueduct

DEWHURST ST

GROVE ST.

FLAX ST.

HOLME ST.

SMIRK ST.

BATH STREET

NEWSHAM STREET

CARLTON STREET

WESTON ST.

Maudland

S.P.

Progress Mill (Cotton)

Shelley Road Mills (Cotton)

Eldon Street Mill (Cotton)

DE LACY STREET

PARKER STREET

Reservoirs

OLD LANCASTER LANE

LANCASTER CANAL, NORTH END

Tanners Brow Brick Works

Tanning Park

STOCKS ROAD

Basin

Maudland Viaduct

Stocks Bridge

GREENING ROAD

Ashton Home

Monastery (Bar off)

Talkethy Hall

Monastery (Bar off)

School

MILL STREET

PRAYERS STREET

BEVERLEY STREET

SWANSEA STREET

D

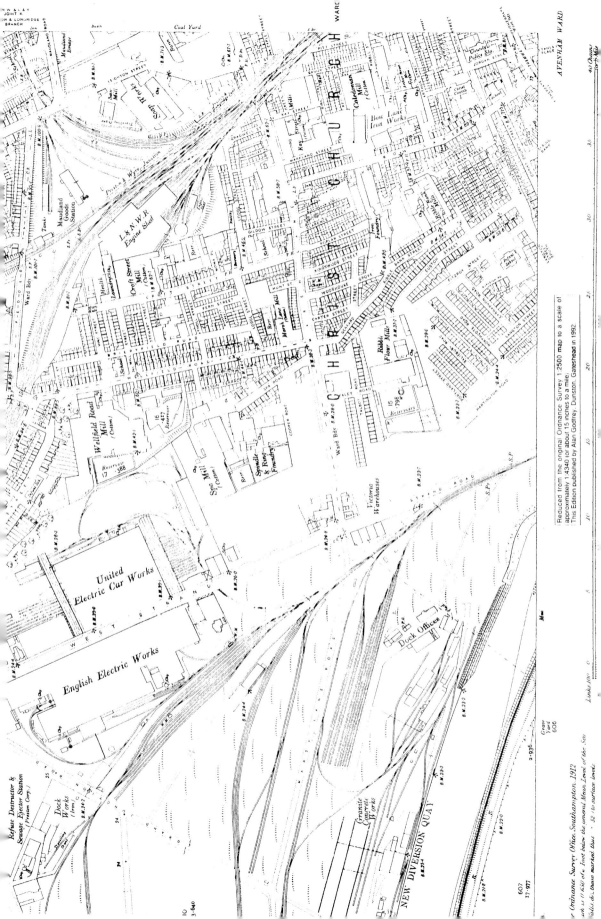

Reduced from the original Ordnance Survey 1:2500 map to a scale of approximately 1:4340 (or about 15 inches to a mile).
This Edition published by Alan Godfrey, Dunston, Gateshead in 1992.

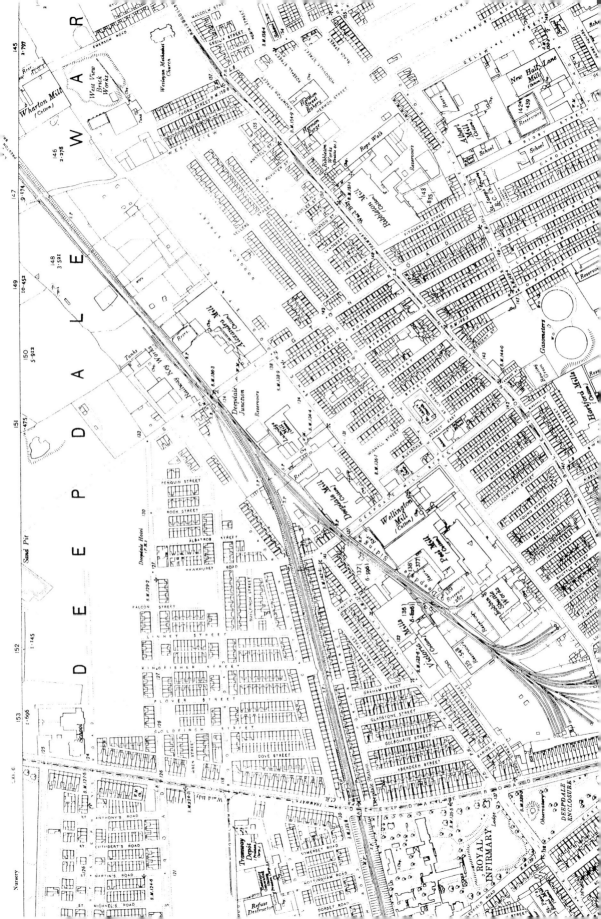

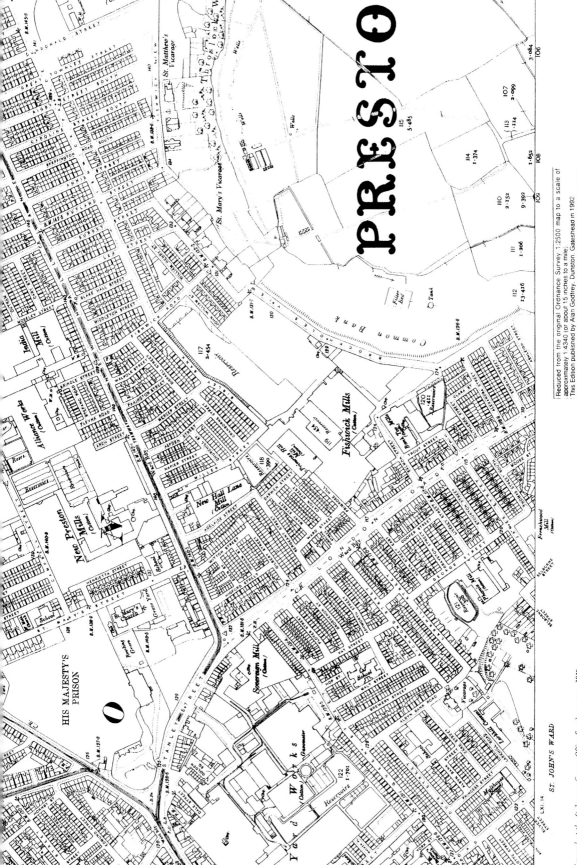

PRESTON

HIS MAJESTY'S PRISON

ST. JOHN'S WARD

Reduced from the original Ordnance Survey 1:2500 map to a scale of approximately 1:4340 (or about 15 inches to a mile).
This Edition published by Alan Godfrey, Dunston, Gateshead in 1992

Director General at the Ordnance Survey Office, Southampton, 1912

Index

Mills

General